WRAP®
FOR THE EFFECTS OF
TRAUMA

MARY ELLEN COPELAND PHD

Author of *Wellness Recovery Action Plan*®
Healing the Trauma of Abuse
WRAP Plus

Peach Press
Dummerston, Vermont

Published by Peach Press, Dummerston, Vermont.

Cover Design and Book Layout by Gamine Graphics.

ISBN: 978-09848326-5-1
Printed in the United States of America

This book is dedicated to the memory of my dear friend,
Irene Alexa,
who taught me so much about dealing with the effects of trauma,
particularly developing and keeping a strong circle of support,
and to people all over the world who are trying to deal
with the effects of all kinds of trauma,
and who are looking for a simple, safe,
self-determined way to do that.

Trauma is anything bad that has happened or is happening to you. It may be just one thing that happened or it may be many things over time. No one else can determine for you how serious this trauma is and how much it is affecting your life. If you are experiencing things like anxiety, despair, alternating high and low moods, hearing voices, seeing things that are not there, delusions, paranoia, phobias, nightmares, night terrors, dissociation, or low self esteem, they may be a result of trauma in your life. It might be trauma that you remember, or trauma that you don't remember. In either case, it is hard to deal with. It disrupts your life. It keeps you from being the kind of person you want to be and doing the things you want to do. Sometimes it feels like the trauma "spoils everything." It is HARD to deal with.

I hope this book will help you heal and move on with your life. It will not tell you what you have to do. But it will help you figure out what you want to do and can do to help yourself.

CONTENTS

PREFACE

For over twenty years, I have been working with people who experience mental health difficulties. This work is a result of my ongoing personal search for wellness and improvement in the quality of my life in spite of challenging mental and physical health issues.

I had always wondered if perhaps the horrible things that happened to me in my life were causing my deep depressions, my low self-esteem, my incapacitating anxiety, my night terrors and nightmares, my incessant flashbacks, my irrational fears. Perhaps it was not mental illness as I had been told, but rather a normal reaction to horrific life events; things like seeing a deadly accident and a dear friend killed when I was 5, like my mother going into a mental institution when I was 8 years old, like being molested and abused by an older male cousin, living with an abusive husband. The list could go on and on as it could for many of us.

Over the years I have talked to more and more people about this, and it is now widely recognized that this is true—that many, many people who experience mental health difficulties are having these issues due to past, recent or even current trauma. They may have been traumatized and been too young or too scared to remember it. When these issues are addressed as trauma-related, rather than caused by a brain disorder, people can, over time, heal, and enjoy recovery, wellness and greater life satisfaction. When you are seeking help, being asked, "What happened to you?" instead of, "What's wrong with you?" facilitates the recovery process.

My own acceptance of trauma as the basis for my mental health difficulties has changed my path. In this book, I will share with you many of the skills and strategies that have been helpful to me in my recovery, and many that I have heard about from other people. Perhaps they will be helpful to you. I expect you have many of your own, and will uncover more as you continue your healing journey. WRAP is, and will always be, the cornerstone of my recovery.

Mary Ellen Copeland

DESCRIPTION OF WRAP®

The Wellness Recovery Action Program is a structured system for monitoring uncomfortable and distressing feelings and behaviors, and through planned responses, reducing, modifying or eliminating them. It also includes plans for responses from others when you cannot make decisions, take care of yourself and keep yourself safe. WRAP has now been intensively studied in rigorous quantitative research studies, and has been listed as an evidence based practice by the National Registry of Evidence-Based Programs and Practices (http://nrepp.samhsa.gov/ViewIntervention.aspx?id=208). The findings of these studies, available at WRAPandRecoveryBooks.com/research prove the efficacy of this system.

This system was developed in 1997 by people who were trying to find ways to relieve their own mental health issues. It has been used since then by people all over the world who have been dealing with mental health challenges, including the effects of trauma. These are people like you who are working hard to feel better and get on with their lives.

Using a three ring binder, a set of tabs or dividers, and lined three ring paper, you develop your own Wellness Toolbox and a six-part monitoring and response system. You can also use another kind of notebook, the forms in this book, the Build Your own WRAP program that is available on-line on our website, or you can use "WRAP for Your Computer"- a CD Rom, which is available online from

WRAPandRecoveryBooks.com. If you choose, you can ask a supporter or health care provider to assist you in developing your WRAP.

You begin the planning process by developing a Wellness Toolbox. A Wellness Toolbox is a listing of skills and strategies that you have used or want to use to keep yourself well and to help yourself feel better when you do not feel well. You will use this list of tools to develop the rest of your Wellness Recovery Action Plan.

Section 1 is a Daily Maintenance plan. Part 1 is a description of how you feel when you feel well. In Part 2, you list everything you need to do every day to maintain your wellness. In Part 3, you list things you might need to consider doing each day to maintain your wellness and enjoy yourself.

Section 2 deals with Triggers. In Part 1, you identify those events or situations that, if they occur, might cause uncomfortable feelings or behaviors. In Part 2, using your Wellness Toolbox for ideas, you develop an action plan of what you can do to help yourself if any of these Triggers occur.

Section 3 deals with Early Warning Signs. In Part 1, you identify subtle signs that you are feeling badly. In Part 2, using your Wellness Toolbox for ideas, you develop a plan of things to do to help yourself feel better when you start noticing these Early Warning Signs.

Because you are experiencing the effects of trauma in your life, you may feel like you are experiencing Early Warning Signs every day. If so, for a while, maybe a long while, you will want to use your Early Warning Signs Action Plan every day as your guide to daily living. That is a good thing. Include lots of things you love to do in your plan, and you will find that you will be getting better and better, and that you will be enjoying your life more and more. Eventually you will be able to use just the Daily Maintenance Plan, but there doesn't need to be a rush about that. Revise this action plan whenever you need to so it continues to work for you.

Section 4, When Things are Breaking Down, deals with signs that indicate to you that you are feeling much worse, yet you are not yet in a crisis. This is a time when you can still take action on your own behalf and do things to help yourself feel better. In Part 2, again using your Wellness Toolbox for ideas, you develop a directive plan for yourself of things to do if any of these signs occur.

The signs you list here may be signs that you are experiencing every day. If that is true for you, you will need to use your When Things are Breaking Down Action Plan for a long time, days, weeks, months or even years. That is a good thing. As long as you include lots of things you love to do, your life will be rich and rewarding. It is much better to do this, follow your own plan, than to live in an institution or spend time in the hospital, or to use invasive and harmful treatments. Your life is still in your control and you can make it the way you want it to be, even though you are working on your recovery.

Section 5 is the Crisis Plan. In this part of the plan, you identify those signs that indicate you can no longer make decisions for yourself, take care of yourself and keep yourself safe. Although this part of the plan is developed by you, it is for use on your behalf by your supporters.

In Part 1 of the Crisis Plan, you describe what you are like when you are well. In Part 2, you identify those signs that indicate that others need to take over responsibility for your care. In Part 3, you name your supporters and identify their roles. In Part 4, you list medications, which, if necessary, are all right with you to take, as well as those that you do not want to take, and the reasons why. In Part 5, you develop a plan that you could use to stay at home, either with community care or in a respite center, instead of hospitalization. In Part 6 you identify the treatment facilities that, if necessary, are agreeable with you, as well as those that are not, and the reasons why. In Part 7, you identify the treatments, which, if necessary, are all right with you, and those which are not, and the reasons why. In Part 8 you describe what you want your supporters to do for you, and just as importantly, what you don't want them to do. In Part 9, you describe for your supporters how they can tell when you no longer need to use your Crisis Plan.

Section 6 is the Post Crisis Plan. It includes a series of questions that guide you through that challenging time when you are healing from a crisis. It walks you step-by-step back to being able to use your Daily Maintenance Plan again.

Many people develop their WRAP in groups led by certified facilitators trained by The Copeland Center for Wellness and Recovery. This is the "evidence-based" way to do it, so you can be assured that the facilitator will follow the values and ethics that support the use of WRAP. However, using this book as a guide, you can develop your WRAP on your own, or with the assistance of a supporter.

For more information about setting up WRAP training, contact http://www.CopelandCenter.com.

Visit http://www.WRAParoundtheWorld.com to find WRAP groups in your area. You may also want to check with local mental health organizations to see if they have any WRAP activities available.

Who Develops Your WRAP?

There is only one person who can develop your WRAP: YOU. You decide if you want to develop a WRAP, when you will develop it, what you will put in it, what you will leave out, and how you will use it.

Who Can Use WRAP?

Anyone can use WRAP. WRAP can be used as a guide to daily living by anyone dealing with the effects of trauma in their lives who wants to create positive change in the way they feel, or increase their enjoyment of life. It may mean you want to effectively manage certain aspects of your life—anything from deep sadness to severe anxiety, from substance abuse to hearing voices, from panic attacks to flashbacks, medical or lifestyle issues, or to increase the level of your wellness. I have described this plan at workshops and conferences and the response is always the same. "This is something I can do for myself, something that will work."

Empowerment—Connection—Validation

When bad things happen to people, when they are traumatized, they often lose a sense of their own personal power, lose their sense of trust in the world and have a difficult time connecting with others, even peers, family members and people they used to consider friends. If this resonates with your experience, you may want to focus on Wellness Tools and Action Plans that support you in the process of:

1. Taking back your own power. You can do this by remembering that this is your WRAP. You decide how you will develop it, when you will develop it, how long you will take to do it, and how you will use it.

2. Taking some safe risks, trying some new things and beginning to slowly and carefully develop a close circle of friends and supporters you can trust.

3. Seeking out people who validate you and your experiences,

people who don't try to convince you that it wasn't all that bad, but who acknowledge that it was horrible and that it is understandable that you are having a hard time.

Getting Started: WRAP® Options

There are many different ways that you can use to develop your WRAP.

They include using:

- a ring type binder—one inch thick will do—dividers or tabs, a supply of binder filler paper and a writing instrument of some kind.

- any notebook or paper, a computer, or voice recorder

- the forms in this book

- the Build Your Own WRAP online program (http://mentalhealthrecovery.com/e-learning/descriptions.php#build)

- "WRAP for your Computer" software program (http://mentalhealthrecovery.com/store/wrapcomputer.html)

You may also choose to have a friend or other supporter give you assistance and feedback as you develop your WRAP—but this is up to you.

If you don't like to write, you could ask someone else to write your plan for you as you tell them what to say.

These and other resources on developing and using WRAP, and mental health recovery, are listed at the end of this book. They can be reviewed online at **www.WRAPandRecoveryBooks.com**.

CHAPTER 1
Developing a Wellness Toolbox

The first step in developing your own WRAP for dealing with the effects of trauma in your life and as a guide to daily living, is to develop a Wellness Toolbox. This is a list of things you have done in the past, or could do, to help yourself stay well; and, things you could do to help yourself feel better when you are not doing well. Hopefully, as you work on your healing, you will discover many wellness tools. You will use these "tools" to develop your own WRAP.

Begin by labeling the first section in your WRAP binder "Wellness Tools." List the tools, strategies and skills you use on a daily basis to keep yourself well, along with those you use frequently or occasionally to help yourself feel better. Include things that you have done in the past, things that you have heard of and thought you might like to try, and things that have been recommended to you by health care providers and other supporters. You can get ideas on other tools from self-help books including those by Mary Ellen Copeland including: *Healing the Trauma of Abuse; The Depression Workbook: A Guide to Living With Depression and Manic Depression; WRAP Plus; The Worry Control Workbook; Winning Against Relapse;* and *The Loneliness Workbook.* You can get other ideas from the CDs, Wellness Tools and WRAP: Step-by-Step and the Wellness Recovery Action Plan DVDs and the website www.WRAPandRecoveryBooks.com. You can also get good ideas by asking others who have had similar experiences, and by asking your health care providers.

The following is a list of some **common** Wellness Tools that others have used to heal from the effects of trauma. If the tool is preceded by an asterisk, you can find more information in the appendices at the back of this book.

However, you may have discovered some **unusual** Wellness Tools that are helpful to you. I have. And I have heard some suggestions from others. I am including a list of those as well. Some of them may work for you, too. And they may help you to think more deeply about what really does work for you. You may be able to come up with some creative Wellness Tools of your own.

There is also a list of examples of Wellness Tools that are things you may want to **avoid**.

These are **only examples**. They are listed here in case you want to try them or use them, and to give you ideas on other Wellness Tools.

Common Wellness Tools

- *Talking to someone who validates you and your experiences
- Going to the library for a free event
- Talking to a health care provider
- *Peer counseling or exchange listening
- *Focusing exercises
- *Relaxation and stress reduction exercises
- *Guided imagery
- *Journaling
- *Creative, affirming activities
- *Exercise
- *Diet
- *Light
- *Extra rest

There is more information on these topics in the Appendix.

- Trying a new recipe
- Time off from home or work responsibilities
- Attending a support group
- Seeing my counselor or sponsor
- Doing something "normal" like washing my hair, shaving or going to work
- Calling a warm or hot line
- Surrounding myself with people who are positive, affirming and loving
- Wearing something that makes me feel good
- Looking through old pictures, scrapbooks and photo albums
- Making a list of my accomplishments
- Spending ten minutes (or however long I want) writing down everything good I can think of about myself
- Doing something that makes me laugh
- Sitting on a bench in the park
- Finding a really great quotation and putting it where I can see it often
- Listing my options
- Doing something special for someone else
- Getting some little things done
- Repeating positive affirmations
- Focusing on and appreciating what is happening right now
- Listening to music, making music or singing
- Creative activities like crafts, needlework, painting, drawing, woodworking, sculpture, photography
- Reading whatever you enjoy like fiction, comics, mystery novels, inspirational writings
- Word puzzles, games
- Going fishing
- Dancing spontaneously
- Quiet time or meditation
- Taking care of something I have been putting off
- Eating my favorite foods

Ideas of **unusual** wellness tools that others have used. Some of these you will want to do in private unless you share your space with understanding people. Anything is OK as long as you do not hurt yourself or anyone else.

- Quickly getting in the shower with my clothes on (a response to feelings of wanting to harm myself)
- Making a list of people who care about me and putting it in my pocket
- Hiding under my covers or hiding anyplace
- Keeping my comforting music handy so I can play it whenever I want
- Writing myself a letter of encouragement and then mailing it to myself
- Sucking my thumb
- Giving myself an affectionate nickname
- Hitting my pillows over and over
- Writing out whatever is bothering me, and then tearing it up
- Screaming loudly until I don't feel like screaming any more
- Coloring in a coloring book (for kids or adults)
- Singing loudly or playing a musical instrument like drums, loudly
- Have someone read something comforting to me, or read it out loud to myself
- Hugging stuffed animals
- Taking a shower and letting my worries go down the drain
- Playing with toys
- Pretending I am a child, or an animal
- Holding a baby or a baby doll
- Asking for as many hugs as I need
- Treating myself as if I were my best friend
- Writing a letter to someone, telling it like it is, and not sending it, or sending it
- Singing inspirational songs in the shower

- Buying myself something I enjoy wearing (thrift stores are good for this)
- Leaving a hopeful note for myself at night, to find in the morning
- Feeling velvety or soft fabric
- Repeating over and over to yourself what a great person you are
- Safely throwing things (one person talked about smashing old dishes into a dumpster)
- Writing words like hope, courage, strength, peace on rocks with a marker

Your list of tools could also include **things you want to avoid**. You may not want to stop doing these things "cold turkey" or stop doing them forever. You can write that into your plan. For instance, a Wellness Tool could be calling your brother on the phone once a week instead of every day. It could mean you smoke fewer cigarettes each day or limit yourself to a certain number of cigarettes a week. If you are used to hurting yourself, it may be that you do it less and less over time.

Avoid or limit:

- Use of alcohol, sugar, and/or nicotine
- Going to bars or places that serve alcohol
- Going to places where you might meet people who could hurt you or who treat you badly
- Getting overtired
- Certain people
- Certain places
- Certain kinds of activities
- Watching the news on TV
- Violent movies and television programs
- The newspaper or certain sections of the newspaper

Add new Wellness Tools whenever you think of them. As you are working on other sections of your WRAP, you will think of Wellness Tools that you may not have included in your original list of Wellness Tools. I suggest you add them to your Wellness Toolbox as you work on the rest of your WRAP. For instance, when I was developing my Daily Maintenance List, I thought about my need to drink 8 glasses of water a day to feel well. So I added it to my list of Wellness Tools.

It's a good idea to have lots of Wellness Tools in operation on a daily basis, and to be adding new ones often. Not only will they increase the quality of your life and your resilience—they are also effective and fun ways to create balance and well-being. If you encounter rough times, it is much easier to increase the number of Wellness Tools you are using, and to turn them into action plans effectively and quickly. If you are hardly using any Wellness Tools at all, then increasing them when you are feeling low will be much more difficult.

Refer to the list of Wellness Tools as you develop your Wellness Recovery Action Plan. Keep it in the front of your binder so you can use it whenever you feel you need to revise all or parts of your plan.

This list is a "gold mine" of ideas for you to use to help yourself feel better in even the worst of times. Mine has been like that for me. Whenever times get really tough and I can't figure out what to do next, I start thinking of my Wellness Tools. I have a list of them hanging on my refrigerator door. I keep my WRAP on my computer. My Wellness Tools are easily accessible there as well. You may think of other places you want to keep a copy of your list of Wellness Tools.

My Wellness Tools

_____

_____

_____

_____

_____

_____

_____

_____

_____

_____

_____

_____

_____

_____

_____

_____

_____

_____

_____

_____

_____

_____

CHAPTER 2
Daily Maintenance Plan

You may have discovered that there are certain Wellness Tools you need to use every day to maintain your wellness. Writing them down and reminding yourself daily to actually do these things is an important first step toward wellness. A Daily Maintenance Plan helps you recognize those Wellness Tools you need to use every day to remain healthy, and then to plan your days accordingly. When things have been going well for a while and then you begin to notice you are starting to feel worse, you can refer back to this list to make sure you are doing all the things you need to do to stay well. When you are starting to feel "out of sorts", you can often trace it back to not doing something on your Daily Maintenance List.

A Daily Maintenance List may seem simplistic and you may be tempted to skip or skim over it. However, most people, like me, find that it is the most important part of their whole plan.

On the first tab write Daily Maintenance List. Insert it in the binder followed by several sheets of filler paper.

Part A. What I'm Like When I'm Feeling Well

On the first page, describe yourself when you are feeling well, or the way you felt before the trauma. If you can't remember what you were like before you experienced the trauma, you can ask others what you were like then. Or you can just write how you would like to be. Do it in list form to make it easy. If you prefer to write it out in sentences, that's fine, too. This plan is yours and you can make it whatever way you want it to be. You can include a picture or pictures of yourself looking the way you want to feel. You can even draw a picture of yourself if you want to, or make a recording of a description of yourself feeling well. You can refer to this list whenever you need to remind yourself of what you want to be like, what you are working towards.

Use whatever words you want to use. The following descriptive words that others have used may help you to think of words that describe you.

Safe	Spiritual
Cozy	Curious
Cheerful	Loving
Playful	Kind
Fun	Sincere
Introverted	Honest
Extroverted	Compassionate
Talkative	Careful
Responsible	Tidy
Content	Sloppy
Thoughtful	Organized
Outgoing	Willing to take risks
Competent	Able to evaluate risks
Capable	A good judge of people
Humorous	Active
Contemplative	Able to relax

What I'm Like When I'm Well

_____

_____

_____

_____

_____

_____

_____

_____

_____

_____

_____

_____

_____

_____

_____

_____

_____

_____

_____

_____

Part B. Things I Need To Do Every Day

On the next page, make a list of Wellness Tools you know you need to use **every day** to keep yourself feeling as well as possible. **This list needs to be easily doable in a day**. They are different for everyone. Some of the tools you choose may address specific recurring trauma-related issues, like being afraid to go outside alone (Wellness Tool idea: spend 10 minutes each day standing outside your door alone), or smoking when you get nervous (Wellness Tool idea: having a glass of water instead of smoking, twice a day).

What you include on this list of things you need to do every day will be specific to your needs and circumstances. Make sure it is possible for you to accomplish in one day everything on the list. Avoid making it too long. The following examples may give you some ideas for Wellness Tools you might include on this list:

- Limit myself to 3 cigarettes a day
- Have cereal, milk and fruit for breakfast
- Eat a healthy lunch and dinner
- Drink at least six-8 ounce glasses of water
- Drink only two cups of caffeinated coffee and have them in the morning
- Avoid alcohol and places that serve alcohol
- Avoid Barry who is always offering me a drink
- Limit my junk foods (processed foods that are high in fat, salt and/or sugar) to 2 servings a day
- Walk briskly for at least ½ hour with a friend or family member
- Meditate for at least 15 minutes
- Write in my journal for at least 15 minutes
- Spend at least ½ hour alone doing something I enjoy doing
- Check in with one person on my list of supporters
- Go to work for at least one half day if it is a work day

■ Do any dishes that need to be done

Other people may try to tell you what to put on this list.
This is your list and should include only those Wellness Tools
*that **you** want to include.*

My Daily Maintenance List

_____

_____

_____

_____

_____

_____

_____

_____

_____

_____

_____

_____

_____

_____

_____

_____

_____

Part C. Things I Might Need To Do

On any given day, there are certain things that might need to be done. These are not the things that need to be done every day, but if you need to do them—and don't—it can be stressful. You are healing from the effects of trauma. This is stressful. You don't need any more stress.

To help avoid the stress of not doing things that need to be taken care of, use the next page in your binder to make a reminder list of things you might need to do on a particular day. You can check through this list every day and then do those things that need to be done.

Following are some examples of things you may want to include on your list of things you may need to do on any particular day:

- Schedule appointments with health care providers
- Contact a particular family member
- Spend extra time doing something I enjoy
- Take the afternoon off
- Go for a long walk
- Spend time with a good friend
- Spend extra time with my partner
- Spend extra time with my children or pets
- Have a peer counseling/exchange listening session
- Go to bed earlier
- Vacuum and dust
- Reduce the clutter in my living space
- Buy groceries
- Do laundry
- Buy myself a treat
- Have some personal time
- Plan something fun for the evening or weekend
- Remember someone's birthday or anniversary
- Call my sponsor
- Go to a twelve-step meeting or support group

While some of these examples might appeal to you, remember—this is your WRAP, so you will write your own personal ideas. Of course, you can include any of the ones given as examples if they seem right to you.

That's the first section of the Plan. You can start using it right now. See how it works for you. If it works well, keep it as it is. If it needs to be changed, revise it whenever you want to.

You will be surprised at how much better you will feel after just taking these positive steps on your own behalf.

Things I Might Need To Do

_____

_____

_____

_____

_____

_____

_____

_____

_____

_____

_____

_____

_____

_____

_____

_____

_____

_____

_____

_____

_____

CHAPTER 3
Triggers

Whether you use the word "triggers" or not, the concept of "triggers" is probably already familiar to you. Over time you have probably become aware that there are things that happen that are outside of your control; external events or circumstances that, if they happen, make you feel very uncomfortable. You may experience things like irrational fears, anxiety, deep sadness, unexplainable elation, and intrusive voices. These are **normal** reactions to the traumatic events in our lives. Everyone has Triggers, but if we don't respond to them and deal with them in some way, our reactions to them may actually get worse and worse over time. They may interfere with our health, well-being and quality of life.

The awareness of this vulnerability, and the development of a plan to deal with triggering events when they come up, increases our ability to cope with them more easily and helps keep our reactions from getting worse, thus avoiding more serious difficulties.

On the next tab write "Triggers" and put in several sheets of binder paper.

On the first page, write down those things that, if they happened, might cause you to start feeling badly or to be upset. Include Triggers that are possible or sure to occur from time to time, or which may already be occurring in your life and that may have upset you in the past.

Note: It is not important to project catastrophic things that might happen, such as war, natural disaster, or a huge personal loss. If those things were to occur, you would use the actions you describe in the Triggers Action Plan more often and increase the length of time you use them.

The following is a list of examples of Triggers that other people have noted.

Some of them may be the same as your Triggers. You will have others that are specific to your circumstances. Thinking of and listing these Triggers may be hard for you. It may remind you of the trauma you have experienced. Don't let that keep you from doing this work. Instead, do it a little bit at a time, as slowly as you need to. After you stop working on it, do something from your list of Wellness Tools, something you love to do. After I worked on my list of Triggers, I called a good friend and we talked about good things that were happening in my life right at that time. You may want to take a walk, pet your dog, or watch a movie. Listing your Triggers may be easier for you if you do it with a supporter or attend a group. You could even do it while you are being supported by a counselor.

- Anniversary dates of losses or trauma
- Seeing or hearing something that reminds you of the trauma
- Certain smells, colors, sounds or places
- Loud voices, people yelling at each other, people fighting
- People treating each other badly
- Being around people who are using alcohol or street drugs
- Traumatic news events that remind you of the trauma
- Others being hurt or treated badly
- Particular people
- A person who looks like someone who hurt me

- Teasing, ridiculing, bullying, harassment
- Seeing bad things happen
- Loss
- Intimacy
- Someone trying to tell me how to run my life
- Self-blame
- Guilt (from saying "No", etc.)
- Seeing blood
- Helicopters
- Loud noises
- Certain clothing

My List of Triggers

_____

_____

_____

_____

_____

_____

_____

_____

_____

_____

_____

_____

On the next page, develop an action plan that lists Wellness Tools you can use to keep these Triggers from overwhelming you and making you feel worse and worse. Refer to your Wellness Toolbox for help. Include tools that have worked for you in the past and ideas you have learned from others, as well as ideas from this book. Include tools that you can use in different circumstances. For instance, if you were on a bus and saw an accident, you couldn't really play your guitar in that moment. You could repeat a positive affirmation like "I am OK" or "I am calm and relaxed" to yourself over and over under your breath. But if you are at home and hear some bad news on the TV, you can turn off the TV. There you can play your guitar, or call a friend to talk, or watch a different program that diverts your attention.

This is a list of Wellness Tools that others have found to be helpful to them in relieving the effects of "Triggers". Perhaps some of them will work for you.

- Make sure I do everything on my Daily Maintenance List
- Call a support person and ask them to listen without interruption while I talk about what happened
- Take several deep breaths
- Count from 100-1
- Visualize the place in the world that I most enjoy being
- Do a focusing exercise*
- Repeat over and over a positive affirmation like "I am safe."
- Cuddle with my pet or stuffed animals
- Watch a movie or sitcom that makes me laugh
- Go for a brisk walk or run
- Peer counsel/exchange listening*
- Work on a creative project
- Write in my journal
- Singing

There are some Triggers that you can anticipate, Triggers that are impossible or difficult to avoid, like anniversary dates, holiday gatherings and impending storms. Preparing in advance for these events can make them easier. A friend of mine always planned a special day doing things she enjoyed with people she loved on the anniversary date of her husband's death. Another friend prepares for storms by inviting someone over, having their favorite pillow and blanket ready, and having a craft ready to work on. If you have to be around someone who is distressing to you, like a particular family member, writing names of people who care about you and putting them in your pocket, writing "courage," "strength" or something on a rock and putting it in your purse or pocket, making sure someone is with you at all times and wearing your comfort clothes, are all things that can be really helpful. If you have to go somewhere or do something that reminds you of trauma, plan for something fun to do after you go there, put your list of people who care about you in your pocket, ask someone to go with you, write about it in your journal before you go, and take something comforting with you like a coin or poem.

Over time you will more easily and quickly notice your Triggers, and become adept at dealing with them using your Wellness Tools. As this happens, you will find that the quality of your life will improve. You will be spending more time doing the things you want to do and being the way you want to be.

My Triggers Action Plan

_____

_____

_____

_____

_____

_____

_____

_____

_____

_____

_____

_____

_____

_____

_____

_____

_____

_____

_____

_____

_____

_____

CHAPTER 4
Early Warning Signs

Early Warning Signs are internal and may be unrelated to reactions to stressful situations. In spite of your best efforts, like doing the things on your Daily Maintenance List, keeping up with things you might need to do, noticing and responding to your Triggers, you may notice that you are not feeling quite right. You are probably beginning to experience Early Warning Signs, subtle signs of change that indicate you need to take some further action to keep yourself feeling well. You may not be able to tell why these signs came up. You may not be aware of any Triggers, or any other reason why you might be feeling "not quite right." It is important to be aware of these times and take action that will help you feel better and keep you from feeling worse.

I used to ignore my Early Warning Signs, expecting that they would diminish on their own. It didn't work. I felt worse and worse. Now I take preventative action as soon as I notice these signs. Identifying these signs helped me to be more aware of them and has made it more possible for me to respond quickly.

Reviewing your Early Warning Signs regularly helps you become more aware of them, allowing you to take action before they worsen.

On the next tab in your binder write "Early Warning Signs." Follow that tab with several sheets of lined paper. On the first page make a list of the Early Warning Signs you have noticed.

Some Early Warning Signs that others who have experienced trauma have noted are listed below. Some of these signs may be more serious for you, and you may want to be list them in the next section of the plan, When Things are Breaking Down. You can decide which section they belong in.

- Nightmares
- Flashbacks
- Excessive worrying
- Losing track of time
- Inability to concentrate
- Increased anxiety and nervousness
- Expecting that something bad is going to happen
- Increased worrying
- Inability to experience pleasure
- Feeling like giving up
- Feeling like I can't relate to anybody, feeling isolated and alone
- Not caring what happens to me
- Avoiding people I like
- Being obsessed with something that doesn't really matter
- Irrational thinking
- Feeling unconnected to my body
- Feeling like smoking or drinking alcohol
- Thinking about spending time with people who treat me badly
- Feeling discouraged, hopeless
- Failing to buckle your seat belt
- Avoiding answering the phone when someone that treats you well is calling
- Overeating or not eating enough
- Unexplainable weepiness
- Compulsive behaviors
- Feeling worthless and inadequate
- Feeling abandoned or rejected

- Feeling unworthy
- Deferring to other people
- Certain smells causing anxiety
- Not being able to sleep well
- Problems eating
- Increased irritability
- Inappropriate humor

If you want, you could ask your supporters to let you know when they notice Early Warning Signs that might have slipped past you. If you are attending a group, having other people describe their Early Warning Signs may help you identify your own.

My Early Warning Signs

On the next pages, using your Wellness Toolbox, develop an action plan that you can use when you notice that you are experiencing any of your Early Warning Signs.

Following is a sample action plan that has been used by a person who is healing from the effects of trauma. It includes some things that they must do, and some things that they might do if they can. You can set your plan up that way if you want to. You may have other ideas about how you want to set up your plan so that it works well for you.

Things I must do

- Take a mental health day from work
- Do the things on my Daily Maintenance Plan whether I feel like it or not
- Check in with my counselor and ask her for ideas on how I might help myself feel better
- Do exchange listening (peer counseling) at least once a day
- Do at least one focusing exercise a day
- Do at least three 10 minute relaxation exercises each day
- Write in my journal for at least 15 minutes each day
- Spend at least 1 hour drawing
- Ask others to take over my household responsibilities for a day
- Play my guitar for at least 15 minutes

Ideas of things I can choose to do if they feel right to me

- Review my list of Wellness Tools and choose several to include in my day
- Go to the art museum
- Check in with my health care provider or counselor
- Get together with some good friends
- Wear cheerful clothes

- Spend time with children and pets
- Go to the movies or watch a good movie at home
- Make a list of things that make you smile and then do some of them
- Take a long nap
- Buy myself something to wear that I feel good in
- Read a good book or watch a good movie
- Dance, sing, listen to good music, play a musical instrument
- Meditate or pray
- Get extra exercise—go swimming, walking, running, etc.
- Go fishing
- Take pictures of things you love
- Make a gratitude list
- Fly a kite

Like other sections of the plan, becoming adept at identifying, noticing and responding to your Early Warning Signs takes time and practice. Keep working on it. You are worth it.

As I mentioned earlier, you may feel that you are experiencing Early Warning Signs every day. If so, use the Early Warning Signs Action Plan every day until you find that you don't need to use it any more. It may be a very long time. That is fine, as long as you are in control and doing what you need to do to stay as well as possible. It may be months or years before you feel like you don't need to use this part of the plan every day. Keep working it, and congratulate yourself every day for your good work. Eventually you will be able to use just the Daily Maintenance Plan most of the time, and just use this part of the plan occasionally. But there is no rush about that.

My Early Warning Signs Action Plan

_____

_____

_____

_____

_____

_____

_____

_____

_____

_____

_____

_____

_____

_____

_____

_____

_____

_____

_____

_____

_____

_____

CHAPTER 5
When Things Are Breaking Down

In spite of your best efforts, you may begin feeling worse and worse. You may know why, or you may not know why. It doesn't matter. The key thing is to **keep yourself and others safe**, and **do what you have to do to help yourself get through this hard, hard time** so you can get back to feeling well and enjoying your life again.

Others used to feel that when people felt this badly, they could not take care of themselves and needed others to take control of their lives. We have learned that even when it may seem to others that we are doing badly, and when we know we feel absolutely terrible, that we are still able to take action in our own behalf. This is a very important time. It is necessary to take immediate action to prevent a crisis (a time when you really cannot take care of yourself). If you a have a plan and follow it, it can keep people from doing things to you that are not helpful, things that might even make you feel worse.

On the next tab in your binder, write, "When Things are Breaking Down." Then make a list of the signs that, for you, mean that things have worsened and are close to the crisis stage.

Others have noted the following signs that indicate to them that "things are breaking down." These signs vary from person to person. What may mean "things are breaking down" to one person may mean a "crisis" to another. You have to decide when you can take care of yourself and when you really need others to take over.

These are some of the signs that others have noticed that tell them it's time to take action:

- Having lots of flashbacks
- Feeling like hurting yourself or someone else
- Feeling like I can't go on
- Seeing things that aren't there
- Feeling like something bad is about to happen
- Being oversensitive and fragile
- Not taking care of my personal needs
- Irrational responses to events and the actions of others
- Feeling very needy
- Being unable to sleep at all
- Wanting to avoid everyone
- Taking risks
- Substance abuse
- Being obsessed with negative thoughts
- Dissociation (blacking out, spacing out, losing time)
- Rage
- Chain-smoking
- Bulimia
- Not being able to feel
- Thinking there is no way out
- Letting other people make decisions for you
- Feeling sad as a way of life
- Being easily triggered
- Believing you are totally incompetent
- Having secrets you can't tell anyone
- Thinking you are ugly
- Feeling fearful much of the time
- Thinking you don't deserve to have anyone treat you well

My Signs That Things are Breaking Down

_____

_____

_____

_____

_____

_____

_____

_____

_____

_____

_____

_____

_____

_____

_____

_____

_____

_____

_____

On the next page, write a plan that you think will help you feel better when you feel this badly. The plan now needs to be very directive with fewer choices and very clear instructions. It is difficult, but not impossible, to get yourself feeling well again when you have been feeling this terrible. Many others have been successful in doing it, and you can be successful too. It takes a lot of hard work but you are worth it.

Sample Plan to Use each Day When I am Feeling this Badly (This is a like a good hospital day, a hospital day where you are working on helping yourself to feel better, supported by helpful care providers, except that you are at home; you know what will help you feel better, and you can do it yourself.)

If these signs come up I need to do all of the following every day until I am feeling better:

- Talk to a supporter for at least 15 minutes
- Arrange for someone to stay with me around the clock until I feel better
- Take action so I cannot hurt myself if I feel worse, such as give my medications, check book, credit cards and car keys to a previously designated friend for safe keeping
- Do everything on my Daily Maintenance List
- Take at least three days off from any work or household responsibilities
- Do two exchange listening sessions
- Write in my journal for at least one half hour
- Do three deep breathing relaxation exercises
- Do two focusing exercises

Ask myself if I need to:

- Have a physical examination
- Have my medications checked
- Get a massage
- Talk to a health care provider or counselor

This may seem difficult. But there is nothing more important for you to do. Family members and friends need to understand what you are doing, how important it is, and to give you the space and support you need to do what you have to do for yourself. Don't let anyone talk you out of it. If people around you are not supportive, you need to be spending time with different people.

This may be the part of the plan you need to use every day for a long time. If so, that is absolutely fine. With a good action plan, you will find that your life is rich and full. As time goes on you may need to revise this action plan to better meet your needs. If it keeps you in your own home, doing the things you want to do and being with the people you want to be with, that is what is most important. And if it keeps you from having to use invasive treatments, and from having crises, and helps you get on with your life, that is all to the good. Give yourself lots of credit for every good thing you do in your own behalf.

My Action Plan for When Things are Breaking Down

_____

_____

_____

_____

_____

_____

_____

_____

_____

_____

_____

_____

_____

_____

_____

_____

_____

_____

_____

_____

_____

_____

_____

CHAPTER 6
Crisis Planning

Using the first four parts of your WRAP as a guide to daily living reduces the chances that you will find yourself in crisis. But it is important to recognize the uncertainties of life, and to understand that in spite of your best planning and assertive action in your own behalf, you could find yourself in a crisis where others will need to take over responsibility for your care. This is a difficult situation, one that no one likes to think about. In a crisis you may feel like you are totally out of control.

Writing a clear Crisis Plan when you are well, to instruct others about how to care for you when you are not feeling well, keeps you taking responsibility for your own care even in the worst of times. It will keep your family members and friends from wasting time trying to figure out what to do for you that will be helpful. Instead, following your instructions, they can quickly take helpful action. It will keep them from wondering whether or not they are doing the right thing for you. It helps insure that your needs will be met and that you will get better as quickly as possible.

Develop the Crisis Plan when you are feeling well. However, most people cannot do it quickly. Decisions like this usually take time, thought, and often collaboration with the people of your choice, care providers, family members, and other supporters. Don't rush the process.

Work at it for a while, then leave it for several days and keep coming back to it until you have developed a plan that you feel has the best chance of working for you. Once you have completed your Crisis Plan, give copies of it to the people you name on the plan as your supporters.

The Crisis Plan differs from the other action plans in that **it will be used by others**. The other four sections of this planning process are implemented by you alone and need not be shared with anyone else unless you want to share them. You can write the other four sections any way you want as long as you can understand what you mean. In writing a Crisis Plan, you need to make it **clear, easy to understand, and legible**.

Over the next few pages, I will share with you information and ideas that others have included on their Crisis Plan. It will help you in developing your Crisis Plan.

Since you are particularly concerned about your trauma-related issues, in developing this plan you need to be mindful of your special needs, and actions that others might take that would be upsetting to you and should be avoided.

On the next tab write Crisis Plan. Insert several sheets of lined paper. The form you can use for this plan follows this section or you can download it online at WRAPandRecoveryBooks. com.

Part 1— What I'm like when I'm feeling well

The first step is describing what you are like when you are well. Of course your family and friends know what you are like. But an emergency room doctor may think your ceaseless chatter is a sign of mania, when you have been talking non-stop since you were a child. Or perhaps you are usually quite introverted. An unsuspecting doctor may see this as depression. Poor decision making or mistreatment could occur.

This is the same as the first section of the Daily Maintenance Plan. You can copy it from there.

In the first section write words or phrases that describe what you are like when you are well.

Descriptive words might include:

talkative	retiring
quiet	intellectual
outgoing	humorous
withdrawn	sensible
adventurous	practical
cautious	energetic
outspoken	compassionate
reserved	responsible
ambitious	reliable

Part 2— Signs that others need to take over

You may find that this is the most difficult part of developing your Crisis Plan. Describe those signs that would indicate to others that they need to take over responsibility for your care and make decisions in your behalf. This is hard for everyone. No one likes to think that anyone will ever have to take over responsibility for them or their care. And yet, through careful, well-developed descriptions, you stay in control even when things seem to be out of control.

Allow yourself plenty of time to complete this section. When you start to feel discouraged or daunted, or you start noticing that you feel like you are "being triggered" or have "Early Warning Signs," set it aside for awhile and use one or several of your Wellness Tools, something fun and diversionary, to help you feel better. Work on this list again when you feel that you can. Your Wellness Tools will be a great help to you in getting through this process. You can work on other sections of the plan and come back to this section from time to time if you choose to do it that way.

Ask your friends, family members and health care providers for input. However, the final determination is always up to you. It may take several months to complete this section.

Be very clear in describing the signs. Don't try to summarize. Use as many words as it takes to describe the behavior. Others are going to need to recognize the behavior, as you may not be able to tell them you are having a hard time.

Your signs might include:

- Inability to recognize family members and friends
- Incorrectly identifying family and friends
- Uncontrollable pacing, unable to stay still
- Very rapid breathing or seeming to be gasping for breath
- Severe agitation where you are unable to stop moving and are repeating very negative statements over and over like "I want to die"
- Inability to stop compulsive behaviors, like constantly counting everything
- Catatonic—unmoving for long periods of time
- Neglecting personal hygiene
- Extreme mood swings daily
- Destroying property
- Endangering others
- Thinking you are someone you are not
- Self-destructive behavior
- Abusive or violent behavior
- Criminal activities
- Substance abuse (define carefully what this means)
- Threatening suicide or acting suicidal
- Not getting out of bed at all (for how long?)
- Refusing to eat or drink (for how long?

Part 3 — Supporters

The next section of the Crisis Plan lists those people who you want to take over for you when the signs you list come up. They can be family members, friends or care providers. When you first develop this plan your supporters may be mostly care providers. But as you work on developing your support system, try and change the list so you rely more heavily on family members and friends. Care providers are not consistently available. They move on to other positions. Using natural supports is less expensive, and more accessible.

Have at least **five people** on your list of supporters. If you have only one or two, they might not be available when you really need them. They could be on vacation, or sick. If you don't have that many supporters now, you may need to work on developing new and closer relationships with people by going to support groups, community activities and volunteering. (See "Developing a Support System" in the appendix.) Keep on developing your Crisis Plan even if you are concerned that you don't have enough supporters. More supporters are in your future. But for now, list those supporters you do have. Add new supporters as you develop these relationships.

Following are some examples of attributes people want from those who take over and make decisions for them:

responsible	optimistic
honest	encouraging
sincere	compassionate
knowledgeable	understanding
calm	trustworthy

You may want to name some people for certain tasks, like taking care of the children, or paying the bills, and others for tasks like staying with you and taking you to health care appointments.

When you list them, you may use the following format:

Name   Connection/role   Phone number

There may be health care providers or family members who have made decisions that were not according to your wishes in the past. They could inadvertently get involved in your care again if you don't include the following:

I **DO NOT** want the following people involved in any way in my care or treatment:

Name   Why you do not want them involved (optional)

Many people like to include a section that describes how they want possible disputes between supporters settled. For instance, you may want to say that a majority of your supporters need to agree, or that a particular person or two people make the determination in that case. Or you may want some organization or agency that you trust to intervene on your behalf.

Part 4— Medication

List the name and phone numbers of your physician or physicians and your pharmacy, and any allergies you may have.

List the medications you are currently using and why you are taking them.

List those medications you would prefer to take if medications or additional medications became necessary, and why you would choose those.

List those medications that would be acceptable to you if medications became necessary, and why you would choose those.

List those medications that should be avoided and give the reasons.

Part 5— Treatments

There may be particular treatments that you would like in a crisis situation and some that you would want to avoid. For instance, many people have very strong feelings about electroconvulsive therapy (ECT)—both positive and negative. Let your supporters know whether or not you want this treatment. The reason may be as simple as "this treatment has or has not worked for me in the past," or you may have some stronger reservations or personal reasons why you do not want a specific treatment.

You may have also found some alternative therapies that have helped as well as some that have not, for example, acupuncture, massage therapy, homeopathy. List those you prefer and those you want to avoid.

Part 6— Home/Community Care/Respite Center Options

THIS SECTION IS *VERY* IMPORTANT.

Many people are setting up plans so that they can stay at home, and still get the care they need if they are in a crisis, by having around the clock care from supporters and regular visits with health care providers. Many community care and respite centers are being set up as an alternative to hospitalization where you can be supported by peers until you feel better and can take care of yourself. Set up a plan so that you can stay at home or in the community and still get the care you need. You may need to talk with others about this and explore options that are available in your community.

Since you are dealing with trauma related issues, this is especially important for you. Going to a hospital or some location you are not familiar with for care and assistance might not be a good idea for you. You will benefit by being at home or in your community with people you know and can trust.

If you need help with this section, reach out to your friends and peers, family members and care providers.

Part 7— Treatment facilities

Hopefully, the plan you developed in Part 6 will work for you and you will not need to use this section. However, it is best to be prepared in case your supporters cannot provide you with the home, community or respite care you need. You may need a safe facility, you may be taking medication that needs to be monitored, or you might even prefer to take part in a program at a treatment facility, provided it is one that you know well and are comfortable with, or has a good reputation.

Using your personal experience and information you have learned through your own research or through talking with others, list those treatment facilities where you would prefer to be hospitalized if that became necessary, and list those you wish to avoid.

Part 8 — Help from others

What I need my supporters to do for me that would help me feel better:

This important section takes a lot of thought. You may want to ask your supporters and other health care providers for ideas. What would really help you when you are having a very difficult time? It may help to uncover these things in conversation with others who have had similar experiences.

Some ideas include:

- Listen to me without giving me advice, judging me or criticizing me
- Hold me—or, Don't touch me
- Let me pace
- Let me yell and scream as much as I want
- Lead me through a relaxation or stress reduction technique
- Do exchange listening with m
- Let me talk and talk and talk as much as I need to
- Take me for a walk if I want to go
- Encourage me to write in my journal
- Provide me with materials so I can draw or paint
- Let me express my feelings without judgment
- Keep me safe
- Keep others safe
- Don't talk to me (or do talk to me)
- Encourage and reassure me
- Have my favorite foods available in case I feel like eating (list what they are-macaroni and cheese, chipped beef on toast or a brownie sundae would be great for me)
- Make sure I get exposure to outdoor light for at least ½ hour daily
- Play comedy videos (list)
- Play good music (list the kind)
- Just let me rest

Chore list

Include **a list of things you need others to do for you**, like feed the pets, take care of the children and get the mail, and who you want to do it.

Things To Avoid

Supporters may decide that some things would help that would really be harmful. List what you have discovered through past experience, or those you feel could worsen the situation. Some examples include:

- Seclusion
- Use of restraints
- Forcing me to do anything
- Trying to entertain me
- Chattering or talking "at me"
- Certain kinds of music (list)
- Certain videos or programs on TV (list)
- Getting angry with me
- Impatience
- Not believing me
- Not listening to me
- Yelling at me
- Judging me

Part 9—When my supporters no longer need to use this plan

When you feel better your supporters will no longer need to follow this plan to keep you safe. Make a list of indicators that your supporters no longer need to follow this plan. Some examples include when I:

- have slept through the night three nights.
- eat at least two good meals a day.
- am reasonable and rational.
- am taking care of my personal hygiene needs.
- can carry on a good conversation.
- keep my living space organized.
- can be in a crowd without being anxious.

You have now completed your Crisis Plan. **Update it** when you learn new information or change your mind about things. Give your supporters new copies of your Crisis Plan each time you revise it.

You can help assure that your Crisis Plan will be followed by signing it in the presence of two witnesses. It will further increase its potential for use if you appoint and name a durable attorney. Since the legality of these documents varies from state to state, you cannot be absolutely sure the plan will be followed. However, it is your best assurance that your wishes will be honored.

You may want to use the form on the following pages to develop your Crisis Plan.

Developing your Crisis Plan is a huge achievement. When you have finished your Crisis Plan do something **BIG** to reward yourself. Take a friend out to eat. Go to the movies. Draw a picture celebrating yourself. Do a dance around the room. Whatever feels right to you.

Crisis Plan

Part 1— What I'm like when I'm feeling well

Describe yourself when you are feeling well.

_____

_____

_____

_____

_____

_____

_____

_____

_____

Part 2— Signs

Describe those signs that would indicate to others that they need to take over responsibility for your care and make decisions in your behalf.

_____

_____

_____

_____

_____

_____

_____

_____

Part 3— Supporters

List those people you want to take over for you when the signs you listed above are obvious. They can be family members, friends or health care providers. Have at least five people on your list of supporters. You may want to name some people for certain tasks like taking care of the children or paying the bills and others for tasks like staying with you and taking you to health care appointments.

Name _____

Connection/role_____Phone number _____

Name _____

Connection/role_____Phone number _____

Name _____

Connection/role_____Phone number _____

Name _____

Connection/role_____Phone number _____

Name _____

Connection/role_____Phone number _____

There may be health care providers, family members, or friends who have made decisions that were not according to your wishes in the past. They could inadvertently get involved if you don't include the following:

I **DO NOT** want the following people involved in any way in my care or treatment:

Name _____

Why you do not want them involved (optional)

_____

_____

Name _____

Why you do not want them involved (optional)

_____

_____

Name _____

Why you do not want them involved (optional)

_____

_____

Settling Disputes Between Supporters

You might like to include a section that describes how you want possible disputes between supporters settled. For instance, you may want to say that a majority need to agree, or that a particular person or two people make the determination.

_____
_____
_____
_____

Part 4— Medication

Physician _____
Phone Number _____

Physician _____
Phone Number _____

Physician _____
Phone Number _____

List the medications you are currently taking and why you are taking them. Include the name of the doctor and the pharmacy.

_____
_____
_____
_____
_____

List those medications you would prefer to take if medications or additional medications became necessary, and why you would choose those.

_____

_____

_____

_____

List those medications that would be acceptable to you if medications became necessary and why you would choose those.

_____

_____

List those medications that must be avoided and give the reasons.

_____

_____

_____

_____

Part 5— Treatments

List treatments that help you feel better and when they should be used.

_____

_____

_____

_____

List treatments you would want to avoid.

_____

_____

_____

_____

Part 6— Home/Community Care/Respite Center

Set up a plan so that you can stay at home or in the community and still get the care and support you need.

_____

_____

_____

_____

_____

_____

_____

_____

_____

_____

_____

_____

_____

_____

_____

_____

Part 7— Treatment Facilities

List treatment facilities where you prefer to be treated or hospitalized if that becomes necessary.

_____

_____

_____

_____

_____

List treatment facilities you want to avoid.

_____

_____

Part 8— Help From Others

List those things that others can do for you that would help you feel better or make you more comfortable.

_____

_____

_____

_____

_____

_____

_____

List those things you need others to do for you and who you want to do what.

_____

_____

_____

_____

_____

_____

_____

_____

_____

List those things that others might do, or have done in the past, that would not help or might make you feel worse.

_____

_____

_____

_____

_____

_____

_____

Part 9— Inactivating the Plan

Describe signs, lack of signs or actions that indicate supporters no longer need to use this plan.

_____
_____
_____
_____
_____
_____
_____

You can help assure that your Crisis Plan will be followed by signing it in the presence of two witnesses. It will further increase its potential for use if you appoint a durable power of attorney.

I developed this plan on (date) _____ with the help of _____.
Any plan with a more recent date supersedes this one.

Signed _____ Date _____

Witness _____ Date _____

Witness _____ Date _____

Attorney _____ Date _____

Durable Power of Attorney (If you have one)

_____

Phone number _____

CHAPTER 7
Post Crisis Plan

The Post Crisis Plan is different from other parts of your Wellness Recovery Action Plan because it is constantly changing as you heal. It is hoped that soon after a crisis you will be feeling much better and therefore your daily activities would be different. You may decide to gradually start using other sections of your WRAP. You might start with the section "When Things are Breaking Down," then go to "Early Warning Signs" and eventually, on whatever timeline works for you, back to using your "Daily Maintenance Plan."

Back in the late 1980s, I was hospitalized repeatedly for deep depression, severe anxiety, flashbacks and other difficult mental health challenges, which I now know were the result of traumatic life experiences, some of which were on-going. Those hospitalizations were somewhat useful. They gave me and my family a much needed break from each other. I got some peer support. I was introduced to some wellness tools, although that is not what they were called at that time, things like stress reduction and relaxation techniques and journaling.

However, any positive effects from these hospitalizations were quickly negated when I got home. Twice, I returned to the hospital within two days of my discharge. Why? When I got home all my family and friends considered that I must be well. I was dropped off at my apartment and spent the next few hours alone. One time a friend who had promised to be there decided I must be napping, and didn't bother to call or come. There was no food. The space was messy and disorganized. I immediately felt overwhelmed and totally discouraged. In addition, there was a message that my employer expected me back at work full time in the next few days.

No matter how you work your way out of a crisis, in a hospital, in a respite facility, in the community or at home, you will need to give your recovery from this difficult time special attention. I have come to believe that, for most of us, it takes as long to recover from a mental health crisis as it would to recover from any other major illness or surgery. You need and deserve assistance and support that can be gradually reduced as you feel better and better. It makes sense that planning for dealing with that critical time would enhance your wellness and insure a rapid recovery.

As with the other parts of the Wellness Recovery Action Plan, it is up to you to decide whether or not you want to develop a Post Crisis Plan. If you decide you want to develop a Post Crisis Plan, it is up to you to decide when you will do it. Like the rest of the plan, the best time to develop some parts of your Post Crisis Plan is when you are feeling quite well. However, there are some questions that can only be answered after the crisis, when you are beginning to feel better—like who needs to be thanked and financial issues you need to resolve.

If you are hospitalized and you don't have a Post Crisis Plan, you may want to develop one with your care providers or on your own before you are discharged—a kind of complete discharge plan. If your hospitalization was involuntary, you may want to ask your care providers to explain any possible discharge conditions and how these conditions would affect your Post Crisis Plan.

You may decide to develop your plan when you are working with a group or with your counselor. You could do it with a supportive family member or friend. Others could give you suggestions or advice if you wish, but the final word should be yours. Or you could do it by yourself. You decide whether or not you want to show your Post Crisis Plan to others. It may be a good idea to share your plan with the people who you want to assist and support you as you heal.

Post Crisis Plan

I will know that I am "out of the crisis" and ready to use this
Post Crisis Plan when I:

_____

_____

_____

_____

_____

_____

_____

How I would like to feel when I have recovered from this
crisis:

(You may want to refer to the first section of your Wellness
Recovery Action Plan—What I am Like When I am Well.
This section may be different from what you felt like
before—your perspective may have changed in this crisis.)

_____

_____

_____

_____

_____

_____

_____

Post Recovery Supporters List

I would like the following people to support me if possible
during this post crisis time:

Who: Phone number: What I need them to do:

_____   _____   _____

_____   _____   _____

_____   _____   _____

_____   _____   _____

_____   _____   _____

If you are being discharged from a treatment facility, do you have a place to go that is safe and comfortable?

___ yes ___ no

If not, what do you need to do to insure that you have a safe comfortable place to go?

_____

_____

_____

_____

_____

If you have been hospitalized, your first few hours at home are very important. Will you feel safe and be safe at home?

___ yes ___ no

If your answer is no, what will you do to insure that you will feel and be safe at home?

_____

_____

_____

_____

_____

I would like _____

or _____ to take me home.

I would like _____

or _____ to stay with me.

When I get home I would like to _____

or _____.

If the following things were in place, it would ease my return:

_____

_____

_____

_____

_____

Things I must take care of as soon as I can:

_____

_____

_____

_____

Things I can ask someone else to do for me:

_____

_____

_____

_____

_____

Things that can wait until I feel better:

_____

_____

_____

_____

Things I need to do for myself every day while I am
recovering from crisis:

_____

_____

_____

_____

_____

_____

Things I might need to do every day while I am recovering
from this crisis:

_____

_____

_____

_____

_____

Things and people I need to avoid while I am recovering
from this crisis:

_____

_____

_____

_____

Signs that I may be beginning to feel worse:

(examples: anxiety, excessive worry, overeating, sleep
disturbances)

_____

_____

_____

_____

Wellness Tools I will use if I am starting to feel worse:

(star those that you must do, the others are choices):

_____

_____

_____

_____

Things I need to do to prevent further repercussions from
this crisis—and when I will do these things:

_____

_____

_____

_____

People I need to thank:
Person: When I will thank them: How I will thank them:

_____

_____

_____

_____

_____

People I need to apologize to:
Person: When I will apologize: How I will apologize:

_____

_____

_____

_____

People with whom I need to make amends:
Person: When I will make amends: How I will make
amends:

_____

_____

_____

_____

_____

Medical, legal, or financial issues that need to be resolved:

Issue: How I plan to resolve this issue:

_____

_____

_____

_____

Things I need to do to prevent further loss:
(canceling credit cards, getting official leave from work if it
was abandoned, cutting ties with destructive friends, etc.)

_____

_____

_____

_____

Signs that this post crisis phase is over and I can return to
using my Daily Maintenance Plan as my guide to things to
do for myself every day:

_____

_____

_____

_____

Changes in the first 4 sections of my Wellness Recovery
Action Plan that might help prevent such a crisis in the
future:

_____

_____

_____

_____

Changes in my Crisis Plan that might ease my recovery:

_____

_____

_____

_____

_____

_____

Changes I want to make in my lifestyle or life goals:

_____

_____

_____

_____

_____

_____

_____

What did I learn from this crisis? _____

_____

_____

_____

_____

_____

Are there changes I want or need to make in my life as a
result of what I have learned?

_____

_____

_____

_____

_____

If so, when and how will I make these changes?

_____

_____

_____

_____

_____

_____

_____

Timetable for Resuming Responsibilities

Develop plans for resuming responsibilities that others may have had to take over or that did not get done while you were having a hard time, things like child care, pet care, your job, cooking and household chores.

SAMPLE

Responsibility: <u>going back to work</u>

Who has been doing this while I was in crisis: <u>co-workers</u>

While I am resuming this responsibility, I need (who):

<u>Jane and Eric</u> to <u>help with record keeping</u>

Plan for resuming:

Steps:

- in three days go back to work for 2 hours a day for five days
- for one week go back to work half time
- for one week work ¾ time
- resume full work schedule

Responsibility: _____

Who has been doing this while I was in crisis: _____

While I am resuming this responsibility, I need (who):
_____to_____

Plan for resuming:

_____

_____

_____

_____

Responsibility: _____

Who has been doing this while I was in crisis: _____

While I am resuming this responsibility, I need (who):
_____to_____

Plan for resuming:

_____

_____

_____

_____

CHAPTER 8
How to Use Your WRAP®

In order to use your WRAP successfully, spend some time every day reviewing the pages, and take action if indicated. Most people report that morning, either before or after breakfast, is the best time to review their plan. As you become familiar with your signs and plans, you will find that the review process takes less time and that you will know how to respond to certain signs without even referring to the book.

How you do this review is up to you. However, most people report that they begin their review with the first page in Section 1, Daily Maintenance Plan, "What You are Like when You are Feeling Well." If you are doing OK, then, that day, you will do the things on your "Daily Maintenance List," the list of things you need to do every day to keep yourself well. Also refer to the page of things you may need to do to see if anything "rings a bell" with you. If it does, make a note to yourself to include it in your day. On some days, I also like to review my Wellness Toolbox. It reminds me of all the resources I have available to me and helps me to remember them. I often add a new Wellness Tool or two that I have discovered.

If you are not feeling as well as you would like to feel, review the other sections of your WRAP to see where the signs you are experiencing fit in. Then use the action plan you have designed for that part of the plan as your guide for the day. You may have to use this plan for many days, even months or years, before you are ready to use your Daily

Maintenance List. That is up to you.

For instance, if you feel very anxious because it is the anniversary date of something horrible that happened to you, you may want to follow your action plan in the Triggers section. If you noticed some Early Warning Signs (subtle signs that you are feeling worse) like increased anxiety or irrational fears, follow the action plan you designed for the Early Warning Signs section. If you notice signs that indicate Things are Breaking Down, like intensive flashbacks, nightmares, or feeling out of touch with your body, follow the action plan you developed for "When Things are Breaking Down."

If you are in a crisis situation, your Crisis Plan will help you and your supporters know this. Either you can let your supporters know you need them to take over, or they will know, from their interactions with you, that it is time for them to take over. This is why having a strong team of supporters is so important. They will observe the signs you have reported and take over responsibility for your care, whether or not you are willing to admit you are in a crisis at that time. Distributing your Crisis Plan to your supporters and discussing it with them is absolutely essential to your safety and well-being. If your supporters don't know each other, you may want to introduce them to each other so they can more easily work together if and when they need to. Some people have gathered their supporters together for a meeting to share and discuss their Crisis Plan with their supporters.

If you have just been through a crisis, refer to your Post Crisis Plan to guide you as you heal from this difficult time. When you feel you are ready, you can return to using the other parts of your Wellness Recovery Action Plan as you did before the crisis.

You may decide you want to be in a WRAP support group to support you as you use your Wellness Recovery Action Plan as your guide to daily living. Check with mental health agencies and organizations in your area to find out if such a group exists. If not, you may want to work with others to get one started. There is information on support groups in the Loneliness Workbook (Copeland, M. 2007 Brattleboro, VT: Peach Press). There are also online groups and Facebook pages that you can use as supports. You can access those through the website www.WRAPandRecoveryBooks.com.

There are many resources you can use to assist you in developing and using your WRAP. There is free information and a complete listing of on-line courses, books, CDs, DVDs and training manuals at the website www.WRAPandRecoveryBooks.com. You can also join an e-mail list to receive regular updates on WRAP and WRAP activities, and a quarterly newsletter.

After using your Wellness Recovery Action Plan for some time, you may decide you want to share this planning process with others. For information on WRAP Facilitator Training, go to www.copelandcenter.com.

APPENDIX

The Appendix contains additional topics that may be helpful to you as you work on developing and using your WRAP.

A. Avoiding Trauma

B. War Related Trauma

C. Indicators that a Relationship is Unhealthy or Unsafe

D. Leaving Unhealthy Relationships

E. Boundaries

F. Choices to Make for Yourself

G. Developing, Keeping and Using a Strong Support System

H. Exchange Listening

I. Focusing

J. Relaxation and Stress Reduction Exercises

K. Creative, Fun, Affirming Activities

L. Journaling

M. Music

N. Diet

O. Exercise

P. Light

Q. Getting a Good Night's Sleep

APPENDIX A
Avoiding Trauma

While it is not possible to totally avoid trauma in your life, there are some things that you can do to lessen the possibility of being traumatized.

- Avoid using internet dating services. Do not agree to meet in person anyone you have met on the internet. Do not share your address or other personal information with people you meet on the internet.
- Do not hold meetings that are open to the public, like support groups, in your home.
- Do not invite anyone to your home until you know them well, and you are sure you are safe with them.
- Have only the street number, not your name, on your mailbox.
- Spend time only with people who treat you well. Avoid people who treat you badly, with whom you feel uncomfortable, or those who violate your boundaries.
- Avoid places where people are using alcohol or illegal substances, places where people congregate that are not safe, or sections of your town that are known for their high crime rate.
- Don't walk outside alone at night or in dangerous areas.
- Carry a cell phone with you so you can easily call 911 if you need to.
- Avoid sharing personal details of your life with anyone until you know them well.

- If you get an uncomfortable feeling when you are with someone, honor yourself and back off, even if you don't understand why you feel that way.
- Say "no" if you feel that is the best thing.
- Avoid hitchhiking. Don't ride in a vehicle with anyone unless you know them well.
- Have secure working locks on the doors and windows in your home and use them when you are at home and when you are not at home. Keep your shades pulled down at night.
- Keep a list of emergency phone numbers on or near your phone.
- If there have been times when you have been in crisis and crisis or emergency services or the police were called for assistance, you may want to contact them proactively. Tell them this has happened to you before and may happen to you again. Show them your Crisis Plan and talk with them about how you want to be treated. If you want to avoid certain things like seclusion, restraint and tasering, tell them that, and tell them how they should work with you instead.
- Know in advance where there is a safe place you can go if you need to and keep that information handy.
- Have alternate routes for leaving your living space in case of emergency.
- Have working smoke and carbon monoxide detectors in your living space.
- Be prepared for natural disasters by keeping supplies of water, non-perishable foods, first aid supplies, flashlights and a battery-powered radio on hand.
- If you use a motor vehicle, have at least half a tank of fuel at all times.
- Develop a support system of people you can trust and reach out to them when you need to. Be supportive of them also.

APPENDIX B
War-Related Trauma

If you have been involved in war, you have probably experienced traumas that may cause you to have particular kinds of Triggers, Early Warning Signs, and signs When Things are Breaking Down. It is important for you to be aware of what they are, and notice when new ones happen, so you can develop effective action plans that you and your supporters can easily and effectively use. You will also want to have a strong Wellness Toolbox and develop your entire WRAP to support you as you empower yourself and start to eliminate some of these traumatic feelings.

Some Triggers that people experience who have war-related trauma are:

Loud noises
Being in dark places
Crowds
Yelling
Being touched unexpectedly
Nightmares
Upsetting news events
Silence

Early Warning Signs that you might be experiencing would include:

Sleeplessness
Being unable to concentrate
Feeling jittery

Being irritable
Not wanting to talk
Isolating
Flashbacks

Signs that Things are Breaking Down would include:

Not wanting to be with people at all
Substance abuse
Uncontrollable anger
Increased nightmares or flashbacks
Being unable to sleep for long periods of time
Feeling very angry
Irrational responses to events and the actions of others

Your action plans will help diminish or eliminate these indicators over time.

Refer to the book *WRAP for Veterans and People in the Military* (Copeland, M. 2008 Dummerston, VT: Peach Press) at www. WRAPandRecoveryBooks.com for more information and ideas.

APPENDIX C
Indicators that a Relationship Is Unhealthy or Unsafe

Adapted from *The Loneliness Workbook* (Copeland, M. 2007. Dummerston, VT: Peach Press)

Making promises that are not kept

Sarcasm and/or putdowns

No compliments except to get something in return

Total lack of interest

Not looking you in the eyes

Spending money secretly

Rudeness

Inappropriate sharing of personal information about others

Doing all the talking and not listening to others

Violation of your boundaries

"Know it all" behavior

Putting others down

Teasing, ridicule, taunts, and threats

"Badmouthing" your friends and family

Lying or dishonesty

Wanting you to be only their friend or wanting you to spend all your time with them

Flirting with your partner

Controlling behavior—wants to know where I am, who I am with and what I am doing

Not wanting to be seen with you in public places

Clinging or very needy—wanting you to take care of them

Inappropriate sexual talk

Leers

Making you feel "creepy," even if you don't know why

Asking questions that make you feel uncomfortable

Substance abuse

Criminal activity

Wanting you to spend all of your time with him or her

Uncomfortable or intimate touching

APPENDIX D
Leaving Unhealthy Relationships

Adapted from *The Loneliness Workbook* (Copeland, M. 2007. Dummerston, VT: Peach Press)

Some of the activities that come up in relationships, like substance abuse, violence and criminal activity, are serious and dangerous. You may need to discontinue such a relationship very quickly to keep yourself and others safe. However, you may be in serious danger if you abruptly try to leave such a relationship. Staying in an abusive relationship is not a good way to avoid loneliness. Never allow yourself to be mistreated or abused in any way. You are in abusive relationship if the other person:

- emotionally, physically or sexually hurts you, forces you to do things against your will or threatens you, your family members, your friends, other people you are closely connected with, your pets or your personal belongings.

- is not respectful of you, and does not treat you with dignity and compassion.

- is violent.

- is involved in criminal activity.

- is critical and/or judgmental of you, teasing, ridiculing, or "putting you down," invalidating your ideas and dreams.

- tries to control you—making decisions for you and insisting on being in charge and puts you under a lot of pressure to do things her or his way.

- is jealous and possessive—checking up on you, accusing you of flirting and interrogating you about casual interactions with others.

- tries to keep you from your friends, family and other activities.

- blames you for their own problems or actions.

- has violent rages or very unpredictable behavior.

- follows you around, wants to know where you are and what you are doing at all times

Unacceptable statements this person might make to you include:

"I told you not to wear that!"

"Don't break up with me, you're the only one who understands me!"

"I'm sorry I hurt you, you just made me so mad."

"You are worthless."

"Who were you talking to after class, what were you talking about, why were you so late?"

"No one else will ever want you."

To keep yourself and others safe as you try to leave such a relationship, call your local law enforcement officials when you can safely do so and describe the situation to them. In addition, it will be helpful if you can take the following steps to protect yourself before trying to get away from this person.

- Always carry a personal cell phone with you set so you can speed dial emergency numbers.

- If you feel that you are in immediate danger, call 911.

- Tell someone you trust about your situation.

- Seek advice, support or services from a shelter for people who are being abused.

- Contact a domestic violence hotline or agency.

- Make a safety plan that includes a place to go, money and people who will support you.

- Provide for the care and protection of other people who have been hurt or threatened, including your children.

You may have to ask the police or emergency services for help and protection in order to leave safely. In addition, you may have to go to a place where you will be protected from this person. Once you are there, do not go back. This may be hard, as you may have left behind things that are important to you. Nothing is more important than your life and the lives of loved ones that are also threatened.

All of this may sound very hard. But it is the best thing to do as soon as you can possibly do it. Remember, your life will get better. You will find new friends and supporters.

APPENDIX E
Boundaries

From *Loneliness Workbook* (Copeland, M. 2007 Dummerston, VT: Peach Press)

People commonly set limits or boundaries in relationships around things like:

- the amount of time spent together
- where time together is spent
- time, number and length of phone calls
- amount of support given
- advice
- connection with family
- amount of physical touch

APPENDIX F
Choices to Make for Yourself

From *Loneliness Workbook* (Copeland, M. 2007 Dummerston, VT: Peach Press)

A healthy relationship is never controlling. There are some choices you must make for yourself alone, even though others may try to influence or control you. When others try to influence you and make these choices for you, it is important that you let them know that these choices are up to you. They may include issues like:

- who you will live with
- who you will be intimate with
- who you will marry
- whether or not you will have children
- who your friends will be
- where you will live
- where you will work
- the kind of education, work or career you will pursue
- the kind of clothes you will wear
- how you will style your hair
- how you will spend your time
- what you will eat
- how you will care for yourself
- what you will do with your leisure time
- what your hobbies and special interests will be

APPENDIX G
Developing, Keeping and Using a Strong Support System

One of the most effective responses to mental health challenges often is reaching out to a very good friend, telling them how you are feeling or sharing an activity with them. It is a powerful Wellness Tool.

Everyone needs and deserves at least several key friends or supporters who:

validate you and your experiences
respect your need for confidentiality
you like, respect and trust, and who like, respect and
    trust you
listen to you
may have interests similar to yours
let you freely express your feelings and emotions
    without judging or criticizing
you can tell "anything" to
give you good advice when you want it
allow you the space to change, grow, make decisions and
    even mistakes
accept your good and bad moods
work with you to figure out what to do next in difficult
    situations
assist you in taking action that will help you feel better

If you have friends or supporters who do these things for you, you are very fortunate. However, you may feel that there is no one you can turn to when you are feeling terrible.

You may feel that there is never anyone you can ask for help, no one who cares about you. It's not hopeless. You can take action to change the situation.

Making friends is a skill like other skills—it can be learned. You may have trouble making friends and developing supporters for a lot of different reasons. They include:

> You don't feel good about yourself, so you can't imagine that anyone would like you. If you don't feel good about yourself and it keeps you from having friends and supporters, get a good book on raising self-esteem and work on it until you feel better about yourself. *WRAP Plus* (Copeland, M. 2010 Dummerston, VT: Peach Press) has a good section on self-esteem.

> You expect your friends to be perfect, and so you can't find anyone who meets your standards. If this is true for you, work on changing your attitude. A positive affirmation that counteracts that negative thought is "No one is perfect. There are many wonderful people who would like to be my friend and supporter."

> You are shy and don't know how to reach out to others. Practice being comfortable with others by joining a school club, church group or community group.

> You are sensitive to any sign of rejection, and react to it by giving up on the other person. Avoid giving up on people until you are absolutely sure they can't be supportive. Talk to others about what you are feeling, and encourage them to share how they are feeling. Work together so you can both feel good in the relationship.

> You have not had the opportunity to develop the social skills necessary to make and keep friends and supporters. If you feel this may be the case, discuss it with someone you trust. Tell this person that you have

a hard time getting and keeping friends and supporters and ask them if there is something you are doing that is "turning others off." Be prepared for them to give you an honest answer. Once you know what the problem is, you can work on correcting it.

Avoid blaming others and becoming overly dependent on one or just a few people.

Develop new friends and supporters by:

- joining a community activity or special interest
- group
- listening closely to others when they are sharing with you—everyone likes a good listener
- volunteer
- taking a course
- going to sports events, plays, concerts, movies
- accepting others as they are without trying to change them
- validating others and their experiences

Be cautious about developing friendships online, in bars and social clubs. If you have any concerns that the person you're connecting with might not be a good choice, limit or avoid further contact. Focus on developing friendships with people with whom you feel comfortable and safe.

Making the Connection

Once you have met someone you like and who seems to like being with you, make plans to spend time together. Each time you get together, end that time by making a plan for the next time you will be together. If something comes up you want to share in the meantime, you can arrange a get-together by phone or in person, but always have something planned.

Don't overwhelm the person with phone calls. Use your intuition and common sense to determine when to call and how often. Don't ever call late at night or early in the morning until you both have agreed to be available to each other at those times.

As you feel more and more comfortable with the other person, you will find that you talk more and share more personal information. Make sure you have a mutual understanding that anything the two of you discuss that is personal is absolutely confidential, and never make fun of what the other person thinks or feels. Always let the other person know that you understand when something is hard for them. Don't try to convince them that something is not hard for them when it is. Validate the other person and their experiences. Ask and expect them to validate you and your experiences.

Key Points about Supportive Situations

- Let the supporter know what you want and need. For instance, you may say, "Today I need you to just listen to me" or "Today I need you to validate that that things that happened to me were awful"

- Spend as much time listening and paying attention to your friends and supporters as they spend paying attention and listening to you.

- Spend most of your time with supporters doing fun, interesting activities together.

- Take turns suggesting and initiating activities.

- Keep regular contact with your friends, even when things are going well.

- Don't interrupt when someone is sharing something that is important or upsetting to them.

Keys to Keeping a Strong Support System

Once you have built a strong support system, how are you going to keep it strong?

1. Do everything you can to keep yourself well and stable. Make your wellness your highest priority. Others often don't have a lot of patience with people who don't take good care of themselves.

2. Work on changing any bad habits you have identified that keep people from wanting to be your friends or supporters.

3. Be mutually supportive. Be there for others when they need you, and ask them to be there for you when you need them. Do fun and interesting things together for no reason at all.

4. Try exchange listening with your friends or supporters. See the next section, Exchange Listening.

5. Validate the other person's experiences and how they are feeling, and ask them to validate your experiences and feelings. Seek out friends who are good "validators" and be one yourself.

6. Have a goal of having at least five good friends or supporters. Make a list of your support team members with phone numbers. When we most need to reach out, it is hardest to remember who our friends and supporters are, or to find their phone number. You can have copies of the list of your supporters on your phone and computer, on your bedside table and in your pocket.

APPENDIX H
Exchange Listening

Exchange listening is a structured way of getting the attention and support you need when you are having a hard time or when you are trying to cope with the stress of daily living. It provides an opportunity to express yourself any way you choose, while supported by a trusted friend and ally. It is also great to do exchange listening on a regular basis with a friend or supporter, so you can let your feelings out in a caring and safe environment. Exchange listening is a great way to build a strong friendship.

Exchange listening is a wonderful technique that can help you express your feelings, understand your problems, discover some helpful actions you can take, and even to feel better. When used consistently, it is a free, safe and effective self-help tool that encourages expression of feelings and emotions.

Exchange Listening Sessions

In an exchange listening session, two people who like and trust each other agree to spend a previously agreed upon amount of time together, dividing the time equally, and paying attention to each other's issues. For instance, if you have decided you will spend an hour together, the first half hour is focused on one person and the second half hour on the other person.

It is understood that the content of these sessions is strictly confidential. Judging, criticizing and giving of advice are not allowed.

Sessions should be held in a comfortable, quiet atmosphere where there will be no interruption or distraction, and where the session cannot be heard by others. Disconnect the phone, turn off the radio and television, and do whatever is necessary to eliminate distractions. While most of us prefer sessions where we meet in person, they can be held over the phone when necessary.

The content of the session is determined by the person who is receiving attention—the talker. The talker can use their time any way they choose. It may include eager talk, tears, crying, trembling, perspiration, indignant storming, laughter, reluctant talk, yawning, shaking, singing, wrestling, or punching a pillow. You may want to spend some time planning your life and goals. The only thing that is NOT OK is being rude to or hurting the person who is listening, or hurting yourself.

Often, as the talker, you may find it most useful to focus on one issue and keep coming back to it despite feelings of wanting to avoid it. At other times you may find yourself switching from subject to subject. At the beginning of a session you may want to focus on one particular issue, but as you proceed, you may find other issues coming up that take precedence. All of this is up to you.

The person who is listening and paying attention needs to do only that, be an attentive, supportive listener.

In exchange listening, the expression of emotion is never seen as a sign of a serious illness. Many of us feel that supporters view expression of emotion as meaning that something is wrong with us rather than as a vital part of the wellness process. We have been treated inappropriately for expressing emotion. We may have learned not to express emotion because it is not safe, thus interfering with our wellness process.

Counteracting Self Criticism

You may notice that when you are exchange listening, you say the same negative things about yourself over and over again. This is not helpful, and could even make you feel worse. When you realize you are doing this, or the listener points it out to you, change the negative statements to positive ones and repeat these statements over and over again in the exchange listening session. Before long you will know that these positive statements are true and you will eventually feel better, even though at first it may make you feel worse.

Focusing Attention on the Present

When uncomfortable feelings are keeping you from doing the things you need to do and the things you enjoy doing, you may want to focus listening sessions on getting things back in order in your life and to focus your attention away from past issues. Sometimes it helps to focus your session on the present, putting your attention on pleasant things and your life as it is now.

Keep the session contained so that other time can be used to do things that make you feel good and to manage your life.

The session can be kept contained by the following activities:

1. At the beginning of a session the listener can reinforce the good that is happening in a person's life by asking them to share several good things that have happened in the last week (or day, or month, etc.). This provides a starting point for the session.

2. At the end of the session the person who is listening

brings the other person back to focus on the present by asking them to share something they are looking forward to.

APPENDIX I
Focusing

Focusing is a simple, safe, free, non-invasive yet powerful self-help technique that can help you feel better.

The focusing sequence uses a series of well-defined questions or steps to help you focus on the real issue, the one of most importance at a given time, not what you may be thinking **should** be the real issue. It connects you with the feelings generated by that issue. When connection with the feelings are made and explored, a positive change in feeling is achieved. The result is an understanding at a new level that translates into you're feeling better.

The following is an example of a focusing exercise:

1. Get ready for a focusing exercise by settling down in a comfortable space and asking yourself, "How does it feel inside my body right now?" Search around inside your body to notice any feelings of uneasiness or discomfort and focus your attention on these feelings for a few moments.

2. Ask yourself, "What's between me and feeling fine?" Don't answer; let the feeling that comes in your body do the answering. As each concern comes up, put it aside, like making a mental list. Ask yourself, "Except for these things, am I fine?"

3. Review the list. See which problem stands out, that seems to be begging for your attention. It may be different from the one you thought was most important.

Ask yourself if it's ok to focus on the problem. If the answer is yes, notice what you sense in your body when you recall the whole of that problem. (If the answer is no, choose another problem that stands out and let the other alone for the time being.) Sense all the feeling of the problem. Really feel it in your body for several minutes.

4. Let a word, phrase, or image that matches the feeling of this problem come into your mind.

5. Go back and forth between the word, phrase or image and the feeling in your body. Do they really match? If they don't, find another word, phrase or image that does feel like a match. When they match, go back and forth several times between the word, phrase or image and the feeling in your body. If the feeling in your body changes, follow it with your attention—notice it. Be with the feeling for several moments.

6. If you want, ask yourself the following questions about the problem to help yourself get a change in the way you feel:

- How does the worst of this feel in my body?
- What needs to happen inside me for this whole thing to change?
- What would feel like a small step forward with all this?
- What would feel like a breath of fresh air in thiswhole thing?
- How would it feel inside if this were all ok?
- What needs to change inside me for this to feel better?

7. Be with the feelings that came up for a few moments. Then ask yourself, "Am I ready to stop or should I do another round of focusing?" If you are going to stop, relax for a few minutes and notice how your feelings have changed before resuming your regular activities.

This is a very simple, safe exercise. It tends to become more effective the more you do it. Someone else can read the instructions to you or you can record them and play them back to yourself. Before long you will know them so this won't be a problem.

APPENDIX J
Relaxation and Stress Reduction Exercises

Use of relaxation and stress reduction techniques are an excellent way to help yourself feel better. Learn how to relax when you are feeling well. Practice regularly.

Learning how to relax in our fast paced society, where everyone expects us to be always working hard, is not easy. The best way to do it is to take a stress reduction and relaxation course or class. They are often offered free at hospitals or health care centers. Watch the newspaper for announcements. You can also learn on your own by doing the exercises in this section.

In order to be effective, it is a good idea to practice relaxation daily at a regular time. You will figure out for yourself the times when you would be able to take a 15 minute (or longer) break without interruption. Ask others in your household to respect this time by being quiet and not disturbing you. If you miss a time now and again don't fret. Just do the best you can. Practice relaxing until it becomes second nature, and until you can use it any time you begin to feel nervous, tense or irritable, or if you just want to slow down the pace of your life.

Locate a space or several spaces in your home that are cozy, comfortable and quiet, where you can be away from the concerns of your life. It may be in your bedroom. Relaxing outdoors in a secluded place in the woods, a meadow, by the ocean or on a mountaintop is also a good idea.

When you notice you are feeling badly, spend more time using your relaxation techniques and do them more often during the day. At these times, it is helpful to use a recording with a guided relaxation exercise as a guide.

Try the following relaxation exercises. See which ones help you feel better. (If any of these exercises make you feel worse, stop doing the exercise and try a different one).

Breathing Awareness—Lie down on the floor, with your legs flat or bent at the knees, your arms at your sides palms up and your eyes closed. Breathe through your nose if you can. Focus on your breathing. Place your hand on the place that seems to rise and fall the most as you breathe. If this place is on your chest, you need to practice breathing more deeply so that your abdomen rises and falls most noticeably. When you are nervous or anxious you tend to breathe short, shallow breaths in the upper chest. Now place both hands on your abdomen and notice how your abdomen rises and falls with each breath. Notice if your chest is moving in harmony with your abdomen. Continue to do this for several minutes. Get up slowly. This is something you can do during a break at work. If you can't lie down, you can do it sitting in a chair.

Deep Breathing—This exercise can be practiced in a variety of positions. However, it is most effective if you can do it lying down with your knees bent and your spine straight. After lying down, scan your body for tension. Place one hand on your abdomen and one hand on your chest. Inhale slowly and deeply through your nose into your abdomen to push up your hand as much as feels comfortable. Your chest should only move a little in response to the movement in your abdomen. When you feel at ease with your breathing, inhale through your nose and exhale through your mouth, making a relaxing whooshing sound as you gently blow out. This will relax your mouth, tongue and jaw. Continue taking long, slow deep breaths which raise and lower your abdomen. As you become more and more relaxed, focus on the sound and feeling of your breathing. Continue this deep breathing for five or ten minutes at a time, once or twice a day. At the end of each session, scan your body for tension. As you become used to this exercise, you can practice it wherever you happen to be in a standing, sitting or lying position. Use it whenever you feel tense.

The Inner Exploration—Pick a part of your body on which to focus all your attention. Explore that part of your body in detail with your mind. What are the sensations in this part of your body? How does it move? What does it do? Is it tense? If it is tense, practice relaxing this part of your body. You may want to choose parts of your body that tend to be tense such as the neck, shoulders, jaw, forehead or lower back. Or you may choose internal areas that tend to be tense, such as the stomach or chest. Another idea is to focus on body parts that you rarely think about, such as your toes, your elbows or behind your knees.

Being Present in the Moment—Most of the stress in our lives comes from thinking about the past or worrying about the future. When all of your attention is focused in the present moment or on what you are doing right now, there is no room to feel anything else. When meditating, all of your attention is focused on the present moment. When other thoughts intrude just turn your awareness back to the present. It is not necessary to be alone in a special place to focus all your attention on the moment. Try doing it when you are feeling irritated waiting in a line, stopped at a street light, stuck in traffic, feeling overwhelmed or worried. Notice how this makes you feel.

Progressive Relaxation— The purpose of this technique is to get you to focus on body sensations and how relaxation feels, by systematically tensing and then relaxing muscle groups of your body. Make a recording of this exercise so you can use it when you need to. Leave yourself time on the recording to tense and relax your muscles. Find a quiet space where you will not be disturbed. You can do it either lying on your back or sitting in a chair, as long as you are comfortable.

Close your eyes. Now clench your right fist as tightly as you can. Be aware of the tension as you do so. Keep it clenched for a moment. Now relax.

Feel the looseness in your right hand and compare it to the tension you felt previously. Tense your right fist again, then relax it, and again, notice the difference.

Now clench your left fist as tightly as you can. Be aware of the tension as you do so. Keep it clenched for a moment. Now relax. Feel the looseness in your left hand and compare it to the tension you felt previously. Tense your left fist again, relax it and again, notice the difference.

Bend your elbows and tense your biceps as hard as you can. Notice the feeling of tightness. Relax and straighten out your arms. Let the relaxation flow through your arms and compare it to the tightness you felt previously. Tense and relax your biceps again.

Wrinkle your forehead as tightly as you can. Now relax it and let it smooth out. Feel your forehead and scalp becoming relaxed. Now frown and notice the tension spreading through your forehead again. Relax and allow your forehead to become smooth.

Close your eyes now and squint them very tightly. Feel the tension. Now relax your eyes. Tense and relax your eyes again. Now let them remain gently closed.

Now clench your jaw, bite hard and feel the tension through your jaw. Now relax your jaw. Your lips will be slightly parted. Notice the difference. Clench and relax again.

Press your tongue against the roof of your mouth. Now relax. Do this again.

Press and purse your lips together. Now relax them. Repeat this.

Feel the relaxation throughout your forehead, scalp, eyes, jaw, tongue, and lips.

Hold your head back as far as it can comfortably go and observe the tightness in the neck. Roll it to the right and notice how the tension moves and changes. Roll your head to the left and notice how the tension moves and changes. Now straighten your head and bring it forward, pressing your chin against your chest. Notice the tension in your throat and the back of your neck. Now relax and allow your shoulders to return to a comfortable position. Allow yourself to feel more and more relaxed. Now shrug your shoulders and hunch your head down between them. Relax your shoulders. Allow them to drop back and feel the relaxation moving through your neck, throat and shoulders; feel the lovely, very deep relaxation.

Give your whole body a chance to relax. Feel how comfortable and heavy it is.

Now breathe in and fill your lungs completely. Hold your breath and notice the tension. Now let your breath out and let your chest become loose. Continue relaxing, breathing gently in and out. Repeat this breathing several times and notice the tension draining out of your body.

Tighten your stomach and hold the tightness. Feel the tension. Now relax your stomach. Now place your hand on your stomach. Breathe deeply into your stomach, pushing your hand up. Hold for a moment and then relax. Now arch your back without straining, keeping the rest of your body as relaxed as possible. Notice the tension in your lower back. Now relax deeper and deeper.

Tighten your buttocks and thighs. Flex your thighs by pressing your heels down as hard as you can. Now relax and notice the difference. Do this again. Now curl your toes down, making your calves tense. Notice the tension. Now relax. Bend your toes toward your face, creating tension in your shins. Relax and notice the difference.

Feel the heaviness throughout your lower body, as the relaxation gets deeper and deeper. Relax your feet, ankles, calves, shins, knees, thighs and buttocks. Now let the relaxation spread to your stomach, lower back and chest. Let go more and more. Experience deeper and deeper relaxation in your shoulders, arms and hands, deeper and deeper. Notice the feeling of looseness and relaxation in your neck, jaws, and all your facial muscles. Now just relax and be aware of how your whole body feels before you return to your other activities.

Guided Imagery— Guided imagery uses your imagination to direct your focus in a way that is relaxing and healing. Try the following guided imagery meditation.

Get in a very comfortable sitting or lying position. Make sure you are warm enough but not too warm, and that you will not be interrupted by the phone, doorbells or needs of others.

Stare at a spot above your head on the ceiling. Take a deep breath in to a count of 8, hold it for a count of 4, and let it out for a count of 8. Do that 2 more times.

Now close your eyes but keep them in the same position they were in when you were staring at the spot on the ceiling.

Breathe in to a count of 8, hold for a count of 4, out for a count of 8.

Now focus on your toes. Let them completely relax. Now move the relaxation slowly up your legs, through your heels and calves to your knees. Now let the warm feeling of relaxation move up your thighs. Feel your whole lower body relaxing. Let the relaxation move very slowly through your buttocks, lower abdomen and lower back.Now feel it moving, very slowly, up your spine and through your abdomen. Now feel the warm relaxation flowing into your chest and upper back.

Let this relaxation flow from your shoulders, down your arms, through your elbows and wrists, out through your hands and fingers. Now let the relaxation go slowly through your throat, up your neck, letting it all soften and relax. Let it now move up into your face. Feel the relaxation fill your jaw, cheek muscles, and around your eyes. Let it move up into your forehead. Now let your whole scalp relax and feel warm and comfortable. Your body is now completely relaxed with the warm feeling of relaxation filling every muscle and cell of your body.

Now picture yourself walking in the sand on the beach on a sunny day. As you stroll along you feel the warmth of the sun on your back. You lay down on the sand. The sand cradles you and feels warm and comfortable on your back. The sun warms your body. You hear the waves crashing against the shore in a steady rhythm. The sound of seagulls calling overhead add to your feeling of blissful contentment.

As you lay here you realize that you are perfectly and completely relaxed. You feel safe and at peace with the world. You know you have the power to relax yourself completely at any time you need to. You know that by completely relaxing, you are giving your body the opportunity to stabilize itself, and that when you wake up you will feel calm, relaxed and able to get on with your tasks for the day.

Now, slowly wiggle your fingers and toes. Gradually open your eyes and resume your activities.

There are many recordings that will guide you through relaxation exercises. These can be purchased at health food stores, bookstores and online.

You can make relaxation exercises for yourself by recording one of the relaxation exercises in this book, one from some other resource book or by developing an exercise which feels right for you. You may find it easiest to relax using a recording when you are experiencing uncomfortable feelings, or you just want to feel peaceful and calm.

APPENDIX K
Creative, Fun, Affirming Activities

Creative activities are a simple, safe, fun and affirming way to help reduce uncomfortable feelings.

What are some things that you really enjoy doing, the kind of thing you really get "lost" in, when you are doing them you can't think of anything else? The list of activities that might help you to feel better is extensive. A few ideas include woodworking, knitting, sewing, building models, embroidery, cooking, photography and metal work. Perhaps it's fishing, reading mystery novels, playing the piano, cooking, playing with a pet, or quilting. Make a list of these things for yourself. Hang it on the refrigerator so you can refer to it, or put it in the front of your WRAP book

Any kind of artistic expression you are comfortable with can help you to feel better. Perhaps you enjoy acrylics, watercolors, oils, crayons, magic markers, colored pencils, charcoal, or stick writing in the dirt. Maybe you'd like to work with clay or one of the new synthetic clays. Or you'd like to carve something out of wood or even chisel away at a piece of stone—whatever would feel good to you. Gather together the materials you need and go to it. It helps to have the materials on hand so when you feel like using them they are available.

Remember, you are doing this to help yourself feel better and let out feelings and emotions. It is not to benefit someone else. It is not a piece to be judged or graded.

The hardest thing about these activities is getting started. Make a commitment to try an activity several times. If you enjoy it, make it part of your daily or weekly schedule. If you don't enjoy that one try another. Keep working at it until you've discovered at least several creative activities you enjoy.

For optimum wellness, spend some time every day doing one or more of these activities. You may want to spend a whole day or several days involved in these kinds of activities from time to time.

APPENDIX L
Journaling

People have kept diaries and written accounts of activities, events, dreams, thoughts and feelings for a long time. Recently we have become more aware of the power of this tool in dealing with various kinds of emotional distress. Many people do it regularly no matter how they feel.

All you need to do is get some paper, a pencil or pen, and start to write. Write anything you want, anything you feel. It doesn't have to make sense. It doesn't have to be real. It doesn't need to be interesting. It's all right to repeat yourself over and over. Whatever is written is for you only. It's yours.

You don't have to worry about punctuation, grammar, spelling, penmanship, neatness or staying on the lines. You can scribble all over the page if that makes you feel better. Just keep writing. Draw or paste pictures or words in your journal if you want. Doodle. Anything goes.

Most people choose to keep their journal writings strictly confidential. The privacy of the journal should not be violated by anyone. You don't have to share your writings with anybody unless you want to. Put a note in the front of your journal that says, "This contains private information. Please do not read it without my permission. Thank you!" Some people find it helpful and feel comfortable sharing writings with family members, friends, or health care providers. This is a personal choice.

It helps to set aside a time every day for journaling. It may be early in the morning or before going to sleep at night. Spend as little or as much time writing as you want. Some people like to set a timer.

You can write in your journal any time—daily, several times a day, weekly, before you go to bed, when you wake up, after supper, whenever you feel like it—the choice is yours. You don't have to commit to keeping a journal for the rest of your life—just when you feel like it.

You can write at any speed you want, fast or slow. You can write as much or as little as you want. You can write poems, paragraphs, verse, novels, novellas, fiction, reality, your autobiography, someone else's biography, wishes, fantasies, dreams, beliefs, loves, hates, anything you wish. It can be similar each time or very different.

Have a safe, private place to store your journal, like in the bottom of your underwear drawer or on a high shelf. Other people in your household should respect your right to a private journal. If you do not feel your journal is safe, tear it up each day after you write, put it under lock and key, or give it to a trusted friend. The majority of the power is in the actual writing, so even if you can't keep it close to you, the writing process itself will still have a lot of value.

If you have had a hard time starting to journal, try responding to some of the following questions:

If your life could be any way I want, what would it be like?
What do you LIKE about yourself?
What is making you feel good today?
What made you feel sad today?
What made you feel happy and excited today?
What are the stresses in your life?
What makes you happy?
Who are your favorite people?

Here are some other things you might include in your journal:

> Write a letter to yourself, pretending you are your own best friend.
>
> List the best things that have happened this day (month, year, in your life).
>
> Review something sad that happened to you and give it a happy ending.
>
> The best thing that ever happened to you was:
>
> The worst thing that ever happened to you was:
>
> You are glad to be alive because:

APPENDIX M
Music

Listening to music and making music help people feel better. Think about the kinds of music that help you feel better.

Listening to music on a regular basis is a wonderful Wellness Tool and can help you feel relaxed and peaceful. When you are noticing uncomfortable feelings, spend some time listening to the kinds of music that are most effective for you. Have a collection of music or know the local radio stations that feature music you enjoy.

Making music is also a good way to release feelings and pent-up emotions. Take some time to play any kind of instrument you enjoy playing. You don't have to play perfectly or even well to enjoy playing. You don't need anyone else to critique you. Just play for the sake of playing, for the fun of it.

Drums are great for this purpose. Put on some of your favorite music and then just beat to the rhythm. Enjoy yourself. If you don't have a drum, find something that it is okay to beat a rhythm on and use that.

APPENDIX N
Diet

You may begin to notice that you feel worse after you have eaten certain foods. The most common foods that cause problems are sugar, caffeine, and heavily salted and fatty foods. Some people have difficulty with foods that contain wheat or milk. Become more aware of what you eat. Notice how you feel one half hour or more after you have eaten that food. Make dietary adjustments accordingly. If possible, consult with a nutritionist to find a diet that works well for you. There is lots of great diet information on the internet.

To feel your best, try following these healthy diet guidelines every day. Make substitutions as necessary for your own food sensitivities.

- Eat at least five servings daily of vegetables (about ½ cup each). A big salad every day will help insure that you are getting enough vegetables. Also include at least one or two servings of fruit.

- Eat several servings of whole grain foods.

- Include plenty of protein in your diet, like fish, poultry or other meats, eggs, cheese, beans or soy products.

- Include some dairy products in your daily diet if you are not allergic to them, like milk, yogurt and cheese. Limit or avoid the dairy products that contain lots of sugar, like ice cream and frozen yogurt. They are great for an occasional treat but if you eat them often, you may feel worse. Don't get into the habit of getting an ice cream cone every day on the way home from school or work.

- Replace artificial, refined and processed foods that are low in food value with healthy natural foods.

APPENDIX O
Exercise

Exercise will help you feel better. When you exercise, you will notice that:

- you sleep better
- your memory and ability to concentrate improve
- your uncomfortable feelings decrease
- you feel less irritable and anxious
- your self-esteem increases.

It is often difficult to exercise when you are not feeling well. Even a few minutes of moving will help. Do the best you can. If you can't do it at all right now, don't give yourself a hard time. Begin as soon as you begin to feel a bit better. Listening to music while you exercise may help you feel more energized.

Do whatever it is you enjoy—walking, swimming, skating, rollerblading, skateboarding, surfing, skiing, dancing or playing with your pet. Even outdoor chores such as cutting wood, raking, or gardening, and can help.

You can do the same kind of exercise every day or vary it according to the weather, what you feel like, and things you need to get done. You don't have to join an expensive health club (although it is a wonderful treat if you can afford it). It doesn't have to be strenuous. Even a walk helps.

If you haven't exercised recently or have health problems that may affect your ability to exercise, check with your physician before beginning an exercise program.

APPENDIX P
Light

Have you noticed that you feel worse in the Fall and Winter, or when there are several cloudy days in a row? If you answered yes to these questions and check off several of the following signs, you may have Seasonal Affective Disorder, more commonly known as SAD:

In the Fall and/or Winter, I

_____ lack energy

_____ want to sleep a lot

_____ have difficulty getting out of bed in the morning

_____ am impatient with myself and others

_____ crave sweets and junk food

_____ have difficulty being creative

_____ have difficulty concentrating and focusing my attention

_____ have difficulty getting motivated to do anything

_____ can't get as much done as usual

More people who live in the northern climates (or in the southern hemisphere in the south) have SAD than those who live closer to the equator. If you live in the north, it is even more likely that SAD or lack of light through the eyes is causing part or all of your problem with depression.

In the winter the days are much shorter. We get up and go to school or work in the dark, and come home after dark. Sometimes we don't get out in the daylight at all.

Scientists have found that exposure to sunlight through the eyes helps some people who are depressed to feel better. Being outdoors in the light affects the activity of neurotransmitters in the brain.

If you think you may have SAD, tell your doctor. He or she may be able to give you information on how to treat this disorder. If s/he doesn't know very much about it, ask him/her to refer you to a doctor who does. A physician who knows about light therapy will help you:

- figure out if you have SAD;
- make sure light therapy is appropriate;
- make sure there are no other medical conditions which need treatment;
- work with you to develop treatment that fits your schedule and lifestyle;
- monitor how you are doing;
- provide additional ideas on how you can get more light;
- get needed encouragement and support.

There are some simple, safe, effective things that you can do to help yourself feel better if you have SAD.

1. Spend at least a half hour outside each day even on cloudy days. If you are at school or work, try to spend some time outside during your lunch hour. Glasses, sunglasses or contact lenses will block some of the sunlight you need. If you can't see well enough to go for a walk or be involved in some other outdoor activity without them, sit on a bench eating your lunch or talking to a friend.

2. Gazing at the sky helps, but never look directly at the sun. The amount of light you get outside is enhanced by reflection off snow and reduced by reflection off dark objects such as buildings and trees.

3. Keep your indoor space well lit. Have plenty of lights on. Use full spectrum lights when possible. Let in as much outdoor light as possible. Spend as much time as you can in spaces near windows.

4. Consider using a light box. Learn more about them on the internet. The best time of day to use the light box is in the morning. If you use it in the afternoon or evening, you may notice that you feel irritable, too energized and you may have a hard time sleeping.

Some people notice almost immediate relief when they begin increasing the amount of light they get through their eyes. It usually takes from 4 to 5 days to work, but may take up to 2 weeks.

Tanning booths, which only shed light on the skin, are not recommended for light therapy. They are dangerous, and should be avoided.

APPENDIX Q
Getting a Good Night's Sleep

A good night's sleep will help you feel better. Six to eight hours of sleep a night is enough for most people. (If you sleep too much, you may feel worse).

I have a lot of trouble sleeping. Sometimes I have a hard time getting to sleep. Other times I awaken very early and have a hard time getting back to sleep. I have the most trouble with irrational fears and flashbacks at these times. I have had some success putting myself to sleep by going step by step through a progressive relaxation exercise—starting with my toes. I focus on my toes and relax them. Then I move up to the bottoms of my feet and do the same thing, then the tops. I work my way up my legs and so on. I keep telling myself that I am completely relaxed. Usually I don't get very far with this exercise because I fall asleep.

Another trick I use to try and bore myself to sleep, and to take attention away from my fears and flashbacks, is to play alphabet games. Starting with A, name 4 girls names, then B, and so on. If I am not asleep by the time I finish the alphabet, I start to work on boys names. Or I do the same thing with places, or names that both girls and boys use. Sometimes I do last names of people I know in the same way. It is boring and it eventually puts me to sleep. And it keeps me from thinking about hard times and traumatic experiences.

I have also have had some success putting myself to sleep listening to music or a relaxation exercise on my IPOD. Or I will move to my reclining chair and that change seems to help. I have also used herbal supplements before bedtime with some success.

I have found that I have to change from one sleep strategy to another. Nothing seems to work consistently. As I lie awake, I try not to worry about the fact that I am not sleeping when I should be. That only seems to make it worse.

Some nights I don't get much sleep at all. When that happens, I try to keep a flexible schedule on those days so I don't have to drive very far, don't have any major responsibilities and can take a nap. I consider it an "Early Warning Signs" day and use the Wellness Tools listed in my "Early Warning Signs Action Plan".

The following tips may help you get a good night's sleep.

- Go to bed at the same time every night and get up at the same time every morning. If you get to bed later than usual, get up at the same time anyway. You can take a nap later in the day.

- Avoid "sleeping in." It will probably make you feel worse.

- Avoid or limit the amount of caffeine in your diet. Coffee and tea are not the only culprits. There is enough caffeine in chocolate, some soft drinks and some pain medications to interfere with sleep.

- Avoid the use of nicotine. It is a stimulant. If you cannot give up your smoking habit right now, avoid smoking two to three hours before bedtime.

- Avoid the use of alcohol. While it may help you fall asleep, it will disturb your sleep later and may cause you to awaken early.

- Eat on a regular schedule and avoid a heavy meal prior to going to bed. Don't skip any meals.

- Eat plenty of dairy foods. They contain calcium that helps you sleep. If you can't eat dairy foods, talk to your doctor about calcium supplementation.

- Exercise daily but avoid strenuous or invigorating activity before going to bed.

- When you are trying to get to sleep, play soothing music that shuts off automatically.

- Focus your attention on your breathing and repeat the words "in" and "out" silently as you breathe.

- Read a non-stimulating book or watch a calm television program before going to bed.

- Write in your journal, about anything and everything, until you feel too tired to write any more.

- A turkey sandwich and a glass of milk before bedtime raises your serotonin level (a neurotransmitter) and makes you drowsy.

- A warm bath or shower before going to bed may help you sleep.

- Your local health food store carries a variety of sleep enhancing herbs, and homeopathic preparations that may help you get a good night's sleep.

- A drop of lavender oil on your pillow is relaxing and helps induce sleep.

- If signs of menopause, such as hot flashes and night sweats, are interfering with your sleep, see your health care provider.

FACILITATOR TRAINING MANUAL
Mental Health Recovery including
Wellness Recovery Action Plan® Curriculum

This comprehensive curriculum package, based on years of research and experience, contains a DVD with three videos featuring Mary Ellen, and includes:

Section 1: Instructions for teaching recovery and WRAP®. Includes Values and Ethics.

Section 2: Slides for workshop presentations. Thumbnail sketches and CD.

Section 3: Activities, Handouts, Discussion Topics

Section 4: Mental Health Recovery and WRAP® Group Model

Section 5: Enhancing Learning Opportunities in WRAP groups

The Manual offers detailed information about facilitating Mental Health Recovery and WRAP® classes. This curriculum includes the evidence-based training format used in Mary Ellen's five-day Mental Health Recovery and WRAP Facilitator training. The best preparation for this work is to develop your own personal WRAP® and to attend Facilitator Training offered by The Copeland Center for Wellness and Recovery, or by a Copeland Center certified Advanced Facilitator.

Order online at WRAPandRecoveryBooks.com
Or call: 802.254.2092 $129.00 plus S&H

Copeland Center
FOR WELLNESS AND RECOVERY

Evidence-Based Mental Health Recovery and WRAP®

Dr. Mary Ellen Copeland works exclusively with The Copeland Center for Wellness and Recovery to help you develop facilitators who can provide trainings that meet the criteria of WRAP as an evidence-based practice.

Work with the Copeland Center to set up a Certified WRAP program in your community, agency, organization, corporation or mental health system that meets the rigorous standards that prove the evidence base. These trainings include:

Introduction to Mental Health Recovery and WRAP

WRAP Facilitator Training
5 day training with 2 Advanced Level WRAP Facilitators

Advance Level WRAP Facilitator Training
5 day training with 2 facilitators
Only the Copeland Center is authorized by Dr. Copeland to provide Advance Level Training

Mental Health Recovery and WRAP Refreshers
Designed to meet your specific needs for continuing education and support—recommended at least once every two years

For more information contact the Copeland Center:
info@copelandcenter.com (802) 254-5335
PO Box 6471, Brattleboro, VT 05301
www.copelandcenter.com
To learn more about the WRAP® evidence base, go to
http://nrepp.samhsa.gov/ViewIntervention.aspx?id=208

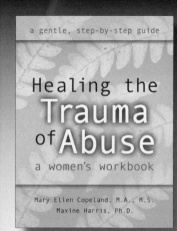

a gentle, step-by-step guide

Healing the
Trauma
of **Abuse**

a women's workbook

Mary Ellen Copeland, M.A., M.S.
Maxine Harris, Ph.D.

Mary Ellen Copeland co-authored the book, *Healing the Trauma of Abuse: A Women's Workbook*, with Maxine Harris of Community Connections in Washington, DC. This important self-help book describes a weekly lesson process (32 lessons in all) that women can use to relieve the effects of trauma in their lives, either when working in a group, with a counselor, or when—as many women must do— working on their own. It rebuilds self-esteem and gives back the personal power, trust, and sense of connection that are taken away by a traumatic event or series of traumatic life experiences, including physical, emotional, and sexual abuse.

Healing the Trauma of Abuse is the beginning of a process—the process of reducing the effects of trauma in your life. It begins by focusing on getting yourself ready to do this work to help insure that your experience is effective and successful.

This workbook is based on the findings of an intensive study of strategies that help women who have been traumatized to heal from the effects of this trauma, and make their lives the way they want them to be.

What's unique about this approach is that it allows you to work your way through trauma recovery at your own pace. It's designed to be used how you wish to use it; you are the expert on yourself so the guidelines on using the workbook are just that, guidelines.

The style and culture of Mary Ellen Copeland's books are based on research, personal experience, information and wisdom gathered over time. The material does not dictate how you should feel or promise quick fixes; it's an exploration of you, your experience, your perspectives and how to use all of that to gain empowerment and control of your future.

$24.95
plus shipping & handling

Available at WRAPandRecoveryBooks.com